Lawrence Archer

THE STORY OF TIRE BEADS AND TIRES

by **WALTER E. BURTON**

Prepared under the sponsorship

of the

NATIONAL-STANDARD COMPANY

Niles, Michigan

THE STORY
OF TIRE BEADS
AND
TIRES

McGraw-Hill

Book Company, Inc.

NEW YORK   TORONTO   LONDON

Library of Congress Catalog Card Number: 53–12050

TITLE-PAGE ILLUSTRATIONS

*As the bicycle and automobile have grown up,
tire and bead developments, though often less
obvious than other details, have kept abreast.
The high-wheeled bicycle had solid-rubber tires
reinforced with wire: the modern Roadmaster
bicycle wears pneumatic tires held in place by
wire beads. The 1900-model Winton automobile
sported soft-bead clincher tires: General Motors'
experimental car "Le Sabre" is equipped with
straight-sidewall tires having carefully engineered
wire-reinforced beads.*

PREFACE

Before the first automobile made its appearance, before, even, the era of the pneumatic tire, wire and rubber had formed a sort of alliance whose chief aim was to hold rubber tires on wheels. Today, that alliance is more important than ever, for practically every rubber tire in use depends on wire to keep it on its rim. The wire is contained in a pair of comparatively little-known but highly important parts of the tire called beads.

In the story of the automobile and its tires, beads have remained dimly in the background. Everyone has read advertisements extolling the virtues of countless tire tread designs: bragging about long mileage records, freedom from blowouts, the wonders of certain types of cords, and (in the earlier days) claiming high resistance to rim-cutting. But how many times have you seen a tire ad that described the virtues, the functions, the really vital role of tire beads? Probably seldom, if ever.

Yet the two beads in every pneumatic tire are the very foundations of that tire. Without them it would be useless. The chief function of the steel wire that forms the heart of every modern tire bead is to hold the tire on its rim—to resist the action of the inflation pressure, which constantly tries to force it off, and the actions of operational stresses, which intermittently strive to accomplish the same thing. The bead foundation of the tire is the connecting link through which the vehicle load is transferred from rim to tire.

Tires can be built and run without treads or cords or breaker strips or white sidewalls, or without the various other well-publicized elements of their make-up. But you would have a difficult time getting around the block on a modern pneumatic tire that somehow had lost its beads. In fact, you wouldn't even get started, for there would be no connection between tire casing and wheel rim.

It is perhaps a paradox that beads, the true foundations of pneumatic tires, have remained the least generally known elements of tire construction. They have behaved much like the silent partner in a company, or the anonymous "angel" who backs a stage show.

But however obscure beads have remained as far as the average person is concerned, to a few men they have been the subject of deep exploration, continual development, and virtually a lifetime of effort. In 1910 the National Cable and Manufacturing Company, predecessor of the present National-Standard Company, of Niles, Michigan, was approached by a rubber company which wanted some wire made for use in straight-side tire beads. From that day on, National-Standard has had bead wire uppermost in its collective mind and has taken a genuine interest in making bead material having proper qualities to suit the needs of rubber companies.

At one time, two National-Standard men, W. F. Harrah (now Honorary Chairman of the Board) and Walter H. Parkin (later President and now Board Chairman) were in personal contact with over 200 manufacturers of automobile tires, each one of which was striving to produce better tires. Throughout the entire period from 1910 to the present time, the company has maintained such contacts with every tire manufacturer and has been interested in virtually every wire-bead problem such manufacturers had to solve.

The long period of working closely with tire makers, and the personal contacts of Mr. Harrah, Mr. Parkin, and of others who joined or followed them, resulted in the gradual accumulation of a fund of bead lore, which ultimately became the background for this book.

The idea for the book was conceived by Mr. Parkin. In 1920, Andy Pennington, who had been a tire-factory superintendent in the early days of the tire industry, joined the National-Standard organization and remained with it until the time of his death. Toward the latter part of his service, Mr. Parkin suggested to him that he write a history of wire used in the beads of tires. This work progressed to a considerable degree but was not completed before Mr. Pennington's death. Then, a few years ago, Mr. Parkin spent a "vacation" developing an outline of a more comprehensive treatment. This ultimately became the basic framework for the present book.

The project of preparing the text, assembling illustrations, and handling the countless other details of creating a book was directed by a group headed by another veteran in the bead-wire field, James C. DeGarmo, National-Standard Vice-President in Charge of Sales. First as a Sales Representative of John A. Roebling's Sons Company, and later while engaged in similar activities for the National-Standard Company, Mr. DeGarmo, over a period of many years, enjoyed a first-hand acquaintance with tire manufacturers and their engineers, designers, and others connected with bead development. The first flat-braided wire used as tire-bead reinforcement was made at Cadiz, Ohio, by Charles S. "Nip" Scott. Following Mr. Scott's death, Mr. DeGarmo operated this plant for a number of years. Old records and notes preserved by Mr. DeGarmo during his long service in the bead-wire field, plus his memory for details, proved invaluable in the preparation of this book.

Another member of the supervising group, K. D. Smith, National-Standard Vice-President in Charge of Rubber Relations, has had a long career in the chemical and tire-design fields. He has served as a teacher of chemistry; and, before joining National-Standard, was engaged in tire-design work for a number of major tire manufacturers. Besides giving valuable technical assistance during the preparation of the book, Mr. Smith, because of his numerous contacts throughout the rubber industry, was able to arrange interviews with engineers and others closely associated with tires and beads.

Robert C. Pierce, another member of the group, and Technical Consultant at National-Standard, is widely known throughout the industry as a designer and inventor. His name has been given to Pierce tape, a type of wire bead reinforcement, because of his work in developing it and in designing machines for its manufacture.

Larry Frazier, Director of Engineering at National-Standard, worked closely with Mr. DeGarmo and the writer in procuring, evaluating, and arranging technical information and illustrations. Besides being well known as the designer of such equipment as tire-building machines and the Frazier head for applying rubber insulation to bead wire. Mr. Frazier is an artist and draftsman of no mean ability. He made the original drawings for a number of the book illustrations and worked closely with artists who prepared the final art.

W. F. Harrah, who has been in active contact with the bead-making industry since 1910, gave valuable assistance, as did company President Alfred H. Johnson. Mr. Parkin kept in touch with the work by checking copy and by offering detailed and helpful criticism.

When, after more than a year of continuous work, the manuscript was nearing completion, the "detail squad," consisting of Mr. DeGarmo, Mr. Frazier, and the writer, was joined by Robert S. Warren of The Griswold-Eshleman Company, advertising consultants. Mr. Warren acted as a coordinator in the task of whipping the accumulation of words and pictures into shape for the actual printing of the volume.

One of Mr. Parkin's primary reasons for planning a book on tire beads is that much of the information concerning details of bead development and construction has been preserved only in the memories of men who have reached the upper age brackets. Many of the very early details have been lost because some of the persons who were familiar with them have passed on. Tire beads have been considered by most people to be merely uninteresting, unglamorous punctuations in the more spectacular story of the automobile. Consequently, few persons who were familiar with beads ever bothered to preserve details about them.

And so, in the gathering of material for this book, much dependence had to be placed on the memories of men in the industry or formerly associated with it—memories which did not always agree with one another. An important pool of information about very early developments in the solid-, cushion-, and pneumatic-tire fields is composed of domestic and foreign patent literature. Such patent material was used as the main source of illustrations for some of the chapters—at the risk of making the book look like a patent digest—because no other sources were available.

Various tire-manufacturing companies were cooperative in providing information and illustrative material, and these are listed elsewhere. Perhaps it may seem to some readers that only comparatively few of the tire manufacturers are featured, or that some companies are played up more than others. There has been no intent to show partiality in this respect. The reason why one company or person is mentioned with respect to a certain bead development, while others are not, may mean that (1) the company or individual mentioned did all the pioneer work concerning the point being discussed, or (2) it is the only source of information that was uncovered. As an example of the first reason, a leading tire company could provide no useful information concerning rim development relating to beads, because it never had engaged in rim manufacture as some of its competitors had. As for the second reason, in more than once instance a tire company could offer no enlightening information concerning certain aspects of bead development because no one in the organization could remember the details or find pertinent records. Perhaps the company, in its early days, had done a lot of work on the phase of bead development being considered; but since then all of the men who were familiar with the work had left either the organization or this world and no one had bothered to make or preserve a written record.

So if this account of tire beads appears to be somewhat vague or tinged with omission in spots, the explanation may lie in the fact that the information available during the preparation of the material was similarly imperfect.

Despite the blank spaces which sometimes were encountered in attempts to run down early bead information, results often were gratifying.

No instance was experienced in which the tire designers, engineers, public relations men, company officials, inventors, and others consulted were unresponsive to requests for information, pictures, and advice. In fact, everyone seemed eager to help; and some of these men must have spent long hours running down dusty facts in old company records and in personal papers. Without such help, the book would not have materialized.

Among the companies and associations which have provided photographs, drawings, information, and assistance are:

Acme Steel Company
Armstrong Tire and Rubber Company
Bridgeport Fabrics, Inc.
Cleveland Welding Company
Dunlop Tire & Rubber Corporation, and Dunlop Rubber Company, Ltd.
Firestone Steel Products Company
The Firestone Tire & Rubber Company
Gates Rubber Company
General Motors Corporation
The General Tire & Rubber Company
The B. F. Goodrich Company
Goodyear Tire & Rubber Company
The Griswold-Eshleman Company
Mansfield Tire and Rubber Company
National Rubber Machinery Company
National Wheel & Rim Association
The Rubber Manufacturers Association, Incorporated
Seiberling Rubber Company
The Tire and Rim Association, Incorporated.
United States Rubber Company

Among individuals who have given valuable assistance in the preparation of this book, in addition to those already mentioned, are:

Hugh Allen, William M. Blackie, Fern Bloom, W. S. Brink, Dr. Arthur Bull, Edward D. Burks, B. Darrow, D. Dunsby, George Flint, John Gammeter, E. H. Gibbs, Harold Gray, William H. Gross, Arthur B. Heibert, Allen Heston, William D. Hines, C. W. Leguillon, Walter Lyon, Herburt W. Maxson, Harold Meyer, W. H. Myers, J. E. McCarty, James McCready, Dr. W. D. Overman, H. P. Partenheimer, R. P. Powers, F. S. Riggs, James Robson, Irvin R. Renner, Clyde Schetter, John M. Schroeder, Peter Seiler, Walter Shively, R. L. Smith, W. Clyde Stevens, J. G. Swain, Joseph Torrey, H. F. van Valkenburgh, James A. Walsh.

Besides the National-Standard Company men already mentioned, numerous other company employees have given assistance whose value can only be estimated—assistance such as the unearthing of obscure data, the procuring of illustrative material, and the checking of technical details.

During the long period of manuscript preparation, contact was made with many persons; and sometimes recollections or records of such incidents may become submerged in the maze of details involved in the production of a book. If, in the attempt to list the names of all persons who have contributed appreciable aid in the preparation of the manuscript and in attendant activities, someone has been omitted, it is purely an oversight.

Walter E. Burton

CONTENTS

CHAPTER 1 § TIRES, BEADS, RIMS

THE MODERN pneumatic tire, taken so much for granted by the average person, is truly a complex structure. Its current form gives scarcely a hint of the countless problems that have marked its development. Many of these problems arose from the necessity of combining several highly dissimilar materials into a finished product that must function as a unit.

The term "tire" often is used to denote the combination of inner tube and outer casing. With respect to the tubeless tire, there is no question but that it refers only to the casing. In this book, the same meaning usually will be implied, and "tire" will refer to the casing only, unless otherwise indicated.

However, a tire, by itself, is of little functional value—except when it is worn out and is used as a bumper on a boat dock, or for some other such purpose. Actually, the tire on an automobile or other vehicle is but a part of the wheel. Ideally, the tire casing, inner tube, wheel rim, wheel disk or spokes, and hub should function as a unit, should behave virtually as if they were made in a single piece and of a single material or at least of harmonious materials. The pneumatic tire is an outstanding example of attempts to get a lot of different things to work harmoniously together. First, the tire casing itself is a complexity of several dissimilar substances: rubber, textile materials, compounding ingredients, and steel, plus relatively small amounts of other metals. Second, the tire is a unique element that must work harmoniously with the rim and other wheel parts. This is where the metal in a tire, in the form of strong wire strands, wire braid, or wire tape, becomes prominent in the picture.

1

PNEUMATIC TIRE STRUCTURE

A TYPICAL pneumatic tire as seen in cross section remotely resembles a horseshoe. The bulk of the section is composed of a textile material such as cotton, rayon, or nylon cord fabric, intermixed with vulcanized rubber compound. The surface normally in contact with the road is the tire tread, made of tough, wear-resisting rubber compound. Rubber extends around and over the sidewalls to form a shield protecting the rubber-fabric skeleton. At the two ends of the tire section, corresponding to the heels of a horseshoe, the edges of the tire casing flare out into roughly triangular shapes to form the beads or beaded edges. In the section, we see that these beads are made prominent by the clusters of steel wires they contain.

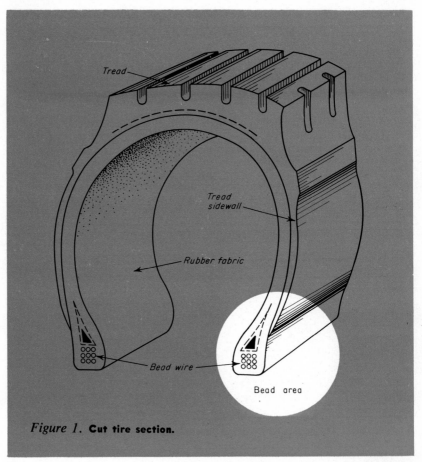

Figure 1. **Cut tire section.**

WHAT IS A "BEAD"?

$\mathcal{T}$HE TERM "bead" is not always a clear-cut one, for it may be interpreted in more than one way. Sometimes a person speaking about the "bead" will be thinking of only the wires which, combined into a stranded ring inside each beaded edge, form the inextensible parts of the tire casing. Another speaker may say "bead" and mean the entire beaded edge: the wire strands; the rubber compound with which the strands are covered and insulated from each other; the textile fabric which, in combination with more rubber, is used to encase the wire and its insulation; and the filler strip, which is made of rubber compound. The filler strip is usually triangular in cross section and is used to fill the space at the apex of the wire group (that is, in the direction of the tread).

The metal reinforcement in a tire is frequently called the grommet or bead-grommet, because it is just that—a steel ring, composed, in modern tires, of wire strands. Formerly or experimentally it was made of various materials ranging from solid steel rods to glass fibers. There may be some who question the fitness of the word "grommet" as applied to tire beads. Perhaps they are thinking only of the grommets, or eyelets, used for reinforcing holes along the edges of a sail or in bathroom shower curtains. But nautical lingo gives us another meaning: the term also denotes a ring or loop made of rope, usually by winding a single strand around and around several times. A bead-grommet is essentially the same, except that its material is steel instead of hemp.

There seems to be no standard term used throughout the industry to denote the bead reinforcement, or bead-grommet. In various factories you will hear such terms as "bead coil," "bead core," "hoop," and "bead ring." While essentially accurate, the last one may be confusing at times because there are parts of tire molds and tire-building machines called "bead rings."

So, if a single interpretation of the term "bead" is required here, it will denote the combination of bead wire, rubber insulation, fabric, wrapping, and flipper strips—these forming the ring-shaped unit that is installed as the "bead" in tire building. A suitable term for that portion of the tire including this bead and the overlying or surrounding rubber and fabric would be "beaded edge." And the word "bead-grommet" seems to be as good a term as any for designating the hoop or ring formed of wire alone or wire insulated with rubber, in modern tires; or of steel rods, flat strips, or other forms in early or experimental tires.

BEAD REINFORCEMENTS TODAY

O VER THE PERIOD of more than a century during which the pneumatic tire has been growing up, almost countless varieties of bead materials and constructions have been tried and sometimes used. But today only one recognized material is employed, in several different ways, for bead reinforcement. That material is wire. Some ways in which it is used in beads are the following:

1. *Single.* A single rubber-covered strand of wire wound around and around to form a stranded, ring-shaped bead-grommet. Also called "Abbott wire" or "Abbott bead."

2. *Weftless.* Several parallel steel wires coated with rubber compound and wound into the form of a stranded ring. The compound holds the strands together while the bead is being manufactured. This construction is also called "fillerless," "pickless," "web tape," and so on.

Figure 2. The clincher tire had soft, stretchable beads containing no wire or other form of metal. Beads were shaped to fit inward-curving rim flanges.

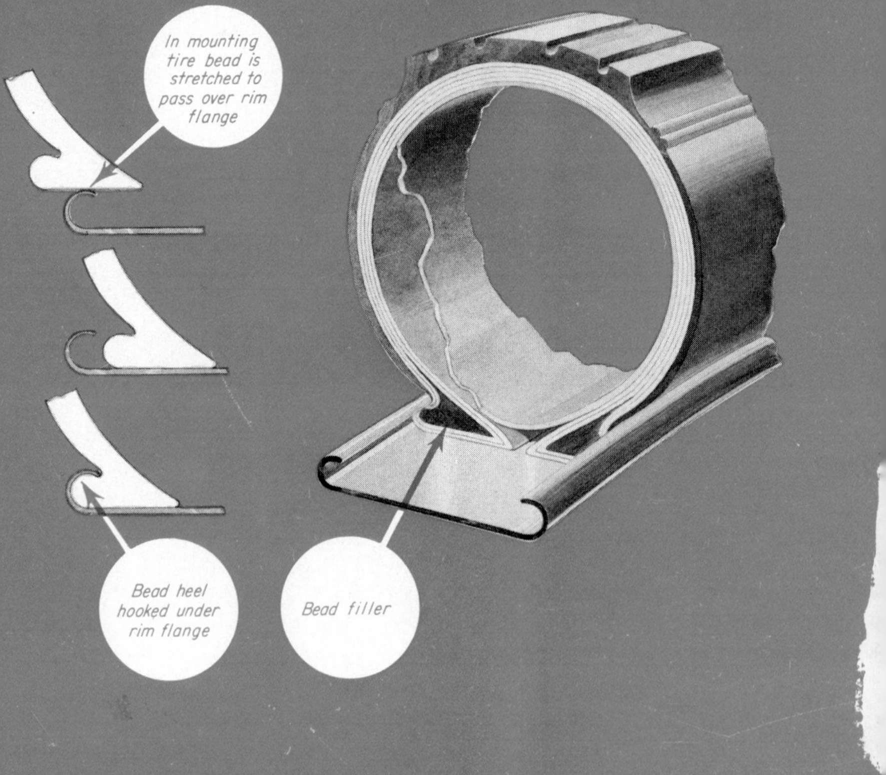

In mounting tire bead is stretched to pass over rim flange

Bead heel hooked under rim flange

Bead filler

3. *Tape*. Three to thirteen parallel straight wires held in the form of a flat tape by a fine filler wire woven back and forth in zigzag pattern, coated with rubber, and wound on a form to produce a stranded ring, annulus, or bead-grommet. The filler wire holds the other wire strands together during processing. This construction is commonly known as "Pierce tape."

4. *Braid*. Thirteen to twenty-one strands of steel wire braided together to form a flat band and then covered with rubber and wound the required number of times around a form, to produce a ring or hoop.

The chief job of the inextensible steel-wire bead-grommets in a modern straight-sidewall tire is to hold the casing on the rim by preventing the beaded edges from stretching. Without the wire, pressure of the air inside the tire would cause the edges of the casing to stretch until they slipped over the rim flanges. Obviously such a tire would be worthless. Thus the bead-grommet, by reacting to the pressure inside the tire, forms, together with other elements of the beaded edge, a rigid, practically inextensible

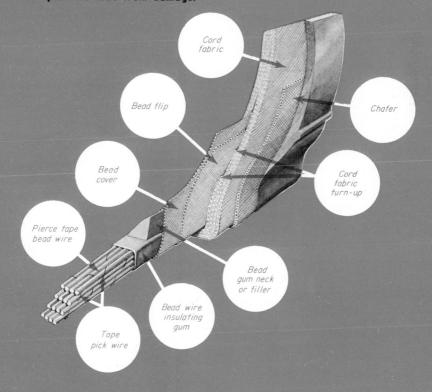

Figure 3. **The straight-side tire has nonstretchable beads containing wire which holds beads tightly against rim. Fabric flap protects tube from damage.**

Cord fabric

Bead flip

Chafer

Bead cover

Cord fabric turn-up

Pierce tape bead wire

Bead gum neck or filler

Bead wire insulating gum

Tape pick wire

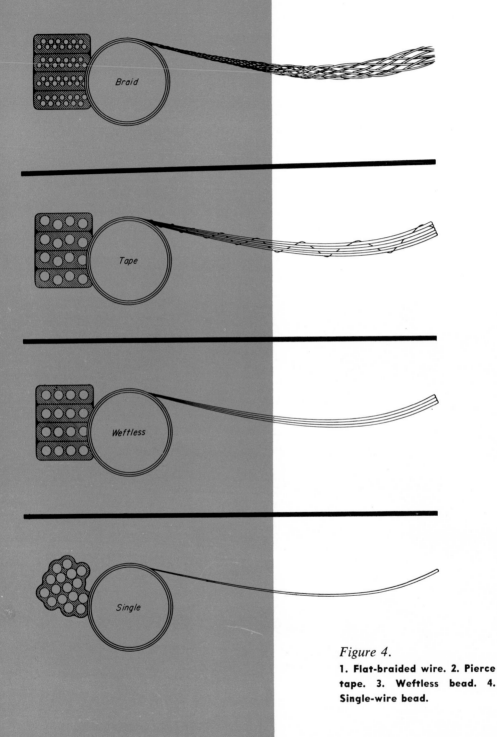

Figure 4.
1. Flat-braided wire. 2. Pierce tape. 3. Weftless bead. 4. Single-wire bead.

foundation supporting the tire load and, in turn, transferring this load to the flanged edges of the rim. Moreover, the bead is a foundation over which the tire is built, and might be likened to the foundation or footing of a house wall. The bead reinforcement, in the form of a stranded-steel hoop or ring, allows a secure anchorage for various textile materials forming plies in the tire carcass. This makes it a practical means of uniting functionally the rubber of the tire and the steel of the wheel rim.

RIMS

THE RIM as generally used today is an integral part of the vehicle wheel. Therefore it is back about where it started. When pneumatic tires first came into use on a "permanent" basis, in the late 1880's, they were

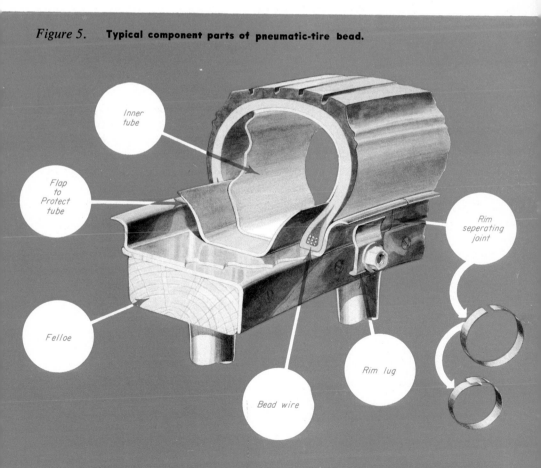

Figure 5. **Typical component parts of pneumatic-tire bead.**

Inner tube

Flap to Protect tube

Rim seperating joint

Felloe

Rim lug

Bead wire

fastened by tape bindings, by bolts, and by numerous other means to the wooden wheel rims, or felloes (called "fellys" in the early days), of wheels, usually those on bicycles or tricycles. Later, the rubber tires were mounted on separate rims which were bolted over the wheel rims, or felloes. Then, still later, tire rim, wheel felloe, and much of the wheel disk merged to become the drop-center unit now used with passenger tires.

Throughout the evolution of the pneumatic tire, virtually as much inventive energy and skill have been expended on rims as on tires. The development of beads and rims has been a hand-in-hand matter, the form taken by the one element invariably depending on the form taken by the other. During a considerable period, a person designing and building a tire had to design and build a rim to match it, for there was little or no standardization which would permit one manufacturer's tires to be used on a rival manufacturer's rims.

TWO MAIN TYPES

WHILE THERE have been countless shapes and styles of rims used in conjunction with automobile tires, two general forms have been most important by reason of their widespread acceptance and use. The clincher rim, whose inward-turning edges formed continuous hooks which engaged matching hooks built into the beaded edges of the tire casing, enjoyed world-wide use for a considerable number of years. Clincher-tire beads contained no wire reinforcement because they had to be stretchable so the tire could be forced over the flange of a standard clincher rim. (On a rim with detachable flange, bead stretchability was not essential, and some clinchers with inextensible, wire-reinforced beads were made.)

The second type of rim that attained world-wide popularity is the straight-side—that is, designed for use with straight-sidewall tires. It was known before the era of the clincher tire, was replaced by the clincher rim, and then in turn replaced it, and today is the type universally used. The straight-side rim has flanges which flare outward instead of inward, and the tire edges have no hooks. The rim flanges serve to keep the tire-casing edges from being forced too far sidewise. The wire bead reinforcement in the tire, being practically inextensible, does what the hook arrangement of the clincher tire and rim was designed to do: it holds the tire on the rim by preventing it from slipping over the flanges.

The tire and rim must be united into a single structure in order to support the vehicle load on a cushion of air. The key element in this union is the wire bead reinforcement.

CHAPTER 2 § THE BEAD APPEARS

A NY ATTEMPT to set a date marking the first appearance of a tire bead will depend somewhat on the way the term "bead" is interpreted. If a specialized edge along the tire structure for the purpose of anchoring it to the wheel is meant, one phase of tire development would be considered. If something involving a metallic reinforcement, made of steel strip or rod, or wire or a combination of wires, is meant, another phase has to be examined.

SOLID AND CUSHION TIRES

THERE ARE some fairly definite signs that the solid-rubber and hollow cushion tires exerted considerable influence on later bead development in the pneumatic tire. Apparently the solid tires on carriages and cycles of the prepneumatic era gave their users considerable trouble, and it was not uncommon for such tires to separate from their wheel felloes or rims at the first opportunity. At any rate, inventors during and after the Civil War era came up with a variety of ideas for holding solid and cushion tires in place. Some of these developments could be considered as involving true beads.

For example, dovetail arrangements were used, the base of the tire flaring out into a dovetail groove running around the felloe. Or the rim edge might be bent inward to form converging flanges, much like later-day clincher rims. One inventor, J. H. Cheever, of New York City, devised a tire of almost semicircular cross section whose edges were gripped by the rim dovetails or flanges, the rounded portion forming the tire tread (see Figure 1). The gripped edges might be called rudimentary beads. Another inventor, J. A. Greene, of Brooklyn, New York, held his tire in place by means of two metal rings fitting in grooves in the wooden wheel felloe, the beveled inner edges of the rings gripping the tire edges which extended partly beneath them.

Various lacing methods were used for holding solid-rubber tires on wheels and were later employed for securing early pneumatic tires. As an example, Daniel Ham, of Iowa City, designed a velocipede-wheel tire that was trough-shaped in section, its sides extending beyond the wheel felloe so laces made of rawhide or other material could be run through them.

WIRE FOR HOLDING TIRES

W IRE WAS recognized early as a logical material for holding tires on wheels. Solid-rubber carriage tires had a tendency to increase their diameters by stretching, thus becoming loose and frequently leaving the wheel. Usually they were mounted in a groove extending circumferentially around the wheel. It was to counteract stretching that inventors such as J. A. Greene added wire rings which, without too much straining of the imagination, can be likened, in purpose at least, to the beads in a present-day tire. Greene proposed that a wire be run through the center of the tire to hold it in the channel of the wheel felloe or rim. He also pointed out that the wire could be flat or twisted instead of round and straight, and that chains or multiple-strand wires or cables could be used (Figure 2).

Rings of wire to lock nonpneumatic tires in place appeared outside the rubber. A bicycle or velocipede tire devised by F. H. Harris, of Toledo, Ohio, rested in a channeled wheel felloe and was secured by two wires running in circumferential grooves molded around each side of the tire. Ends of the wires were bent inward, passed through holes in the rim, and clinched at their tips. Wire length and tension were adjusted so the wires lay within the rim edges and were of lesser circumference than those edges (Figure 3).

In 1888, Thomas B. Jeffery, of Ravenswood, Illinois, suggested lateral projections or beads on a tire, these to be made of metal or hard rubber and shaped so the rim flanges could grip them and thus hold the tire in place.

A development that was to be recalled later, when wire braid was introduced into the tire industry, was the subject of a patent issued to F. E.

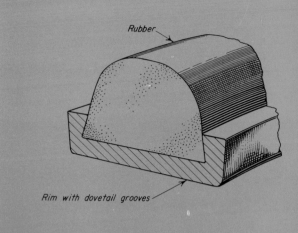

Figure 1.
Solid-rubber tire held by dovetail grooves in rim (J. H. Cheever, patent 86,504).

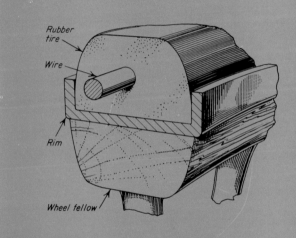

Figure 2.
Single wire run through center of solid tire to hold it securely on rim (J. A. Greene, patent 169,100).

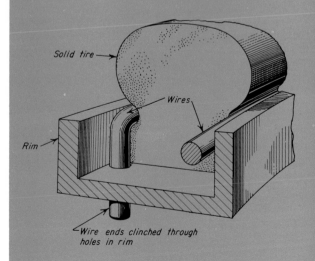

Figure 3.
Two side wires rest on projecting lateral edges of solid-rubber tire to hold jt in rim groove (F. H. Harris, patent 371,580).

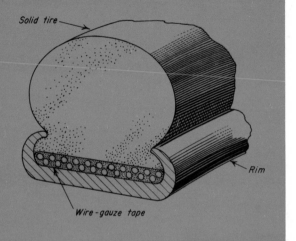

Solid tire

Rim

Wire-gauze tape

Figure 4.

The base of this solid-rubber tire has attached to it a band of wire-gauze tape, flat strip or other material impregnated with soft rubber (Southland and Klauser, patent 420,610).

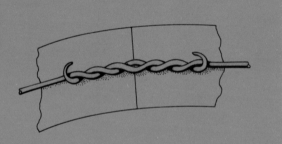

Figure 5.

Sharpened ends of wire form hooks to prevent joint in solid-rubber tire from opening (Jefferies and Grant, patent 449,650).

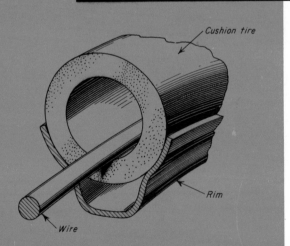

Cushion tire

Rim

Wire

Figure 6.

Solid tire reinforced with endless wire installed on rim whose edges then were forced up around tire to form retaining flanges (George Ahlborn, patent 456,751).

Southland and A. E. Klauser, of Toledo, Ohio, on February 4, 1890. They devised a wire-gauze tape, either rubber-covered or not, which was installed to form the base for a soft-rubber tire vulcanized in place on the wheel rim. The wire gauze, fabric, flat strip, or whatever was used was intended to eliminate some of the troubles that had been experienced with hard-rubber-base tires and with all-soft tires having no reinforcement at all (Figure 4).

MAKING WIRE RINGS

THE PROBLEM of uniting the ends of a wire to form a continuous ring within the solid-rubber tire was the subject of much inventive activity. A common practice was to make the tire as a continuous length of rubber with a hole extending along the center (actually a thick-walled tube), cut it to proper length for the wheel, run a somewhat longer wire through the hole, and force the rubber ends back so the wire could be joined by twisting, brazing, welding, or soldering to form an endless hoop. A pair of inventors, D. P. Jefferies and A. W. Grant, devised a method whereby the twisted wire ends were bent and sharpened to form pointed hooks, which were said to prevent the ends of the tire from separating (Figure 5).

A different angle of attack was to make a ring separately of wire or other forms of metal by brazing the ends together. Then the tire was molded around the ring and placed on a wheel, whose felloe was flattened on the face. Then the felloe edges were spun or otherwise forced around the tire to form retaining flanges. Of course, such tires were not intended to be removable or replaceable (Figure 6). Still another inventor, A. G. Powell, in developing a new bicycle, made his tire in the form of a hollow tube through which he ran a wire ring to hold it on the wheel (Figure 7).

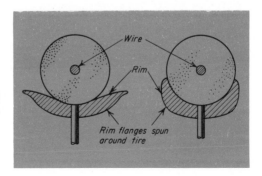

Figure 7.
Cushion tire with wire running through central hole to anchor it on rim (A. G. Powell, patent 452,649).

FIRESTONE SIDE-WIRE TIRE

$\mathcal{M}$ANY OF the numerous ideas proposed by inventors for holding solid or cushion tires on wheels were far from perfect. Some, of course, never reached the point of actual use. Those which did were found, in more than one instance, to contain "bugs" which provided reasons for other inventors to try to solve the tire-holding problem. Wire rings embedded in tires or placed in grooves extending circumferentially around the tires at the sides exerted pressure directly on the rubber. They tended to cut into the rubber, sometimes failed to prevent creeping, and had other shortcomings. In 1900, an invention of James A. Swinehart, of Akron, Ohio, which was intended to reduce such troubles, was brought to the attention of Harvey S. Firestone. This idea was to install short horizontal wires or rods at intervals through the tire rubber near its base (the wires running parallel to the wheel axle), wrap the tire around the wheel groove and fit its ends neatly together, then force an endless wire ring around each side of the tire and over the projecting ends of the cross wires. Outer surfaces of cross wires and inner surfaces of rings were slightly flattened. The ring, or "side wire," tended to force the cross wires toward the wheel felloe, thereby holding the tire in the channel. The idea looked promising to Firestone. Soon after his meeting with Swinehart and others interested in the invention, the Firestone Tire and Rubber Company was born and the side-wire, solid-rubber tire became its first product.

Today you can still see at Akron, Ohio, machines once employed for manufacturing these tires and for installing them on wheels. One machine inserted wire about $\frac{3}{16}$ inch in diameter crosswise in the uncured tire at about 1-inch intervals and then cut each piece to the required length. Another forced the side wires, previously made endless by brazing, into position around the tire and wheel groove and over the cross-wire ends. Side wires ranged from No. 12 for $\frac{3}{4}$- to $\frac{7}{8}$-inch tires, to No. 6 for 2-inch tires.

Figure 8.
Building tire on ring core in era preceding tire-building machines. Beads already have been installed and tread rubber is being rolled down

Figure 9.

**Machine for applying Firestone side-wire tire to carriage
wheel. The solid-rubber tire was secured to the wheel felloe
by means of two endless side wires which were sprung over
the ends of cross wires embedded in the rubber (about 1900).**

PNEUMATIC TIRES

W HILE MANY inventors and tire makers of the day were trying to iron
out the various ills encountered in the use of solid-rubber and cushion
tires on bicycles, tricycles, carriages, and other vehicles, other men were
busy with what was to prove a far more important development in the
long history of the wheel—the pneumatic tire. In this type, rubber turns
the load-carrying job over to air under pressure. The rubber itself,
together with other materials, usually textile in nature, serves largely as a
container and shield against abuse.

16

THE DUNLOP INVENTION

*I*N BELFAST, Ireland, in the summer of 1888, a Scotch veterinary surgeon named John Boyd Dunlop was listening to his young son's complaints about local cycling conditions. The Belfast streets were not nearly so smooth as the cinder cycle paths where grownups pursued their wheeled sport, and the streetcar tracks and rectangular stone paving blocks that the boy had to negotiate between home and school were almost too much for his solid-tired tricycle. Dunlop's son was being shaken to pieces on his trips about town. Besides, he had trouble keeping up with other boys in tricycle races. Could Papa Dunlop do anything about it?

He could—and definitely did. Air, Dr. Dunlop reasoned, is more resilient than solid rubber. So if you take some air and confine it inside a ring-shaped tube. . . . Thereupon he proceeded to assemble a pneumatic tire, the first ever made, he thought. It consisted of an airtight tube of vulcanized rubber surrounded by a casing made of one thickness of "solutioned" fabric—that is, cloth impregnated with rubber dissolved in a solvent and permitted to dry. A valve installed in the tube enabled it to be inflated with air. The tire was bound in place on a wheel with tape wrappings. Dunlop claimed that his new tire would provide a more cushioned ride that would reduce damage to the rider, the tricycle, and the road; that it would require less pedaling energy; and that it would be speedier than solid types. He had proved his point about energy by rolling two wheels with equal force across a yard adjacent to his place of business. One, wearing a solid-rubber tire, rolled a few yards and fell over. The other, equipped with the pneumatic tire, rolled completely across the yard, struck a door, and bounded back a considerable distance.

It is true that before Dr. Dunlop's experiments tires having an air cavity were made and used. These were the "cushion" tires of the day, and were made hollow, with either one or a plurality of cavities in the rubber. But the air in them was simply imprisoned, and not pumped into the cavity or cavities under pressure, as in the true pneumatic tire.

Like almost any new and therefore strange device, Dr. Dunlop's tires were the subject of considerable fun-poking and were nicknamed, among other things, "pudding tires," "mummy tires," and "rags." The latter term probably was inspired by a preponderance of cloth in their outward appearance.

Cycle racing was almost as popular in Belfast in those days as eating,

17

and cyclists began to find that Dunlop's pneumatics would shave worth-while seconds from elapsed times. One such cyclist, named Harvey DuCros, was so impressed with the tire's performance that he formed a new company for its manufacture and sale, and this eventually grew into the extensive Dunlop organization. However, the tape wrappings proved to be lacking in wear resistance and general ruggedness; and so inventors, including Dr. Dunlop himself, began to think of improved ways of build-ing and mounting air-inflated tires.

THOMSON'S PATENT

BUT DR. DUNLOP'S new tire, on which he obtained patents in England and elsewhere, proved to be not so new and revolutionary an idea as the Doctor at first had supposed. Some time after he had got his work on pneumatics under way, there was resurrected a forgotten patent of 1845 dealing with one of those occasional inventions that do not succeed at the moment because they are ahead of their times.

This early patent was issued to Robert William Thomson,[1] a civil engineer of Middlesex, England. This inventor seems to have foreseen an amazing number of improvements and applications dealing with pneu-matic tires. He described his "elastic bearing," or tire, as a "hollow belt" of sulfurized caoutchouc or gutta-percha inflated with air. He pointed out that as a substitute for the metal tire of a wheel, it would require less power, thus rendering motion easier; and that it would be less noisy. His tire consisted of a casing or folds of canvas saturated with rubber solu-tion, sulfurized (cured) by placing it in burning sulfur fumes or immers-ing it in molten sulfur. He suggested other filler materials than air, such as horsehair; and he visioned his tires being used on steam carriages, Bath chairs, rocking chairs, and several others things besides conven-tional wheeled carriages. Thomson seemed to have in mind the modern

[1] Thomson's Specification, which explains his patent No. 10,990 of 1845 (British), is a fascinating document because it covers a surprisingly large territory of ideas involving the use of air-inflated tires. The inventor, back in pre–Civil War days and before the automobile had been developed, hints at or describes such things as truck tires, balloon tires, puncture-resisting tires, pneumatic rollers for moving heavy objects, pneumatic tires for railway trains, air-inflated chair rockers, and pneumatic cushions for Bath chairs. But most significant of all, Thomson covered pretty thoroughly the pneumatic-tire idea, of which he is considered the originator. Many a later inventor wished he had been less thorough. The Thomson Specifica-tion is to be found in standard patent references.

balloon-tire idea, for he recommended relatively large tire sections. A number of Thomson pneumatics were made and used. Among them was a set of 5-inch ones for a brougham of—naturally, in those days—the horse-drawn type.

Thomson's "elastic bearings" never got further, apparently, than the making of some sets for experiment and for use on broughams. Their use was mentioned in the August 22, 1846, issue of *Mechanics Magazine.* But beginning some 40 years later, his patent acted much like a monkey wrench in the machinery of other inventors who attempted to improve rubber tires. Dr. Dunlop in particular apparently found Thomson's patent irksome. The Doctor, it is said, actually believed he had invented the pneumatic tire, until Thomson's patent, like Rip van Winkle, arose from its long slumber. But because he worked at a more opportune time, with an idea that was not ahead of its era, to Dr. Dunlop should go much of the credit for putting air-inflated tires on the wheels and highways of the transportation world. It has been said that the reason Dunlop's tires became a success, whereas Thomson's had faded away, is that beads were developed soon after Dunlop launched his invention.

The pneumatic tire was just a few years behind the solid-rubber tire in making its appearance. Somewhere around 1835 the first solid-rubber tire was made. Then, in 1845, Thomson patented his pneumatic tire.

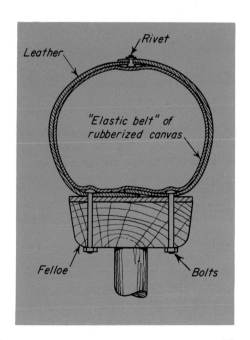

Figure 10.
Cross section of pneumatic tire for carriages, developed by Thomson in 1845 (British patent 10,990).

PNEUMATICS IN AMERICA

*F*OLLOWING CLOSELY on the pneumatic trail of Dr. Dunlop, but on the other side of the Atlantic, was Amos W. Thomas, of Philadelphia. In 1888 and later, he was issued a series of patents on inflated tires. One of his inventions was a single-tube type provided with a pet cock for filling it with air, gas, water, or anything else that was handy (Figure 11). Other Thomas patents included a construction involving inner and outer tubes of rubber, and methods of gluing, binding with rubber or leather bands, or otherwise fastening the tire to the wheel.

During the following 3 years there occurred in England two developments that ultimately had widespread importance in the evolution of the pneumatic tire. One was the invention of the nonextensible bead. The other was the introduction of the clincher tire and rim principle.

FIRST WIRE BEADS

*C*HARLES KINGSTON WELCH was an engineer living in Coventry, England. He designed a pneumatic tire consisting of a canvas-wrapped inner tube and a casing or cover, horseshoe-shaped in cross section, built up of plies of rubberized canvas. There was a rubber tread fastened to the outer circumference by vulcanization. Each edge of the casing was enlarged, and through it ran an endless wire ring, very much like the bead wire in modern tires (Figure 12). Welch devised a metal rim to accommodate his tire. It had grooves in which the beaded edges of the casing rested, and a hollow or drop center for easy tire removal or installation. For his "wired tire," Welch was granted a patent in 1890.

Welch obtained patents in England and the United States on other tire developments, including one covering the use of wire-reinforced beads of smaller diameter than the flange of the wheel rim, or felloe (Figure 13); and a method of covering fabric-sided tires of racing cycles with rubber to reduce damage to the fabric.

While Welch was devising the wire-reinforced bead in England, two other inventors, working independently of him, were doing the same thing in the United States. Alexander T. Brown and George F. Stillman were granted a patent covering a tire whose casing was "made rigid and non-extensible circumferentially" by two ring-shaped wires or beads having

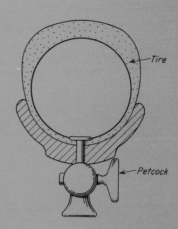

Figure 11.

Tubular tire inflated with air, water, or other fluid by means of pet cock (A. W. Thomas, patent 399,354).

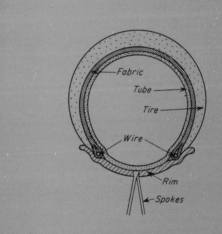

Figure 12.

The Welch tire, with wire-reinforced beads, mounted on a drop-center rim (British patent 14,563).

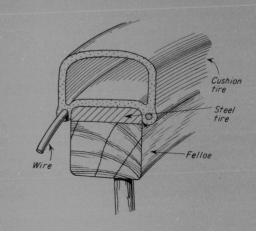

Figure 13.

Welch also devised a cushion tire having wire-reinforced beads overlapping steel tire of carriage wheel (U.S. patent 512,594).

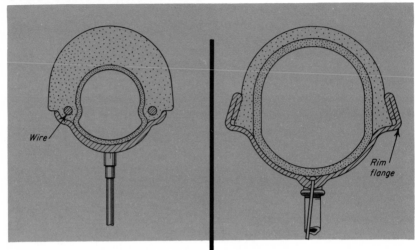

Figure 14.

Brown and Stillman tire having wire-reinforced beads (patent 488,494).

Figure 15.

Later Bartlett used a casing with thickened edges fitting under turned-in flanges (patent 466,532).

joined ends or made endless (Figure 14). These beaded edges rested in grooves in a metal cycle rim, the grooves being below the rim edges but above the bottom of the central part of the rim. The beads were held in place by air pressure within the tube. The Brown-Stillman tire thus used a hollow- or drop-center rim, too.

Eventually both the Welch and Brown-Stillman inventions were held to be valid—another instance of two minds (in this case actually three) with practically a single thought. Rights to both inventions were acquired by the Dunlop organization.

THE CLINCHER TIRE

WILLIAM ERSKINE BARTLETT, an American of Edinburgh, Scotland, Managing Director of the North British Rubber Company, Ltd., came along in 1889 with an idea that was later to be adopted and used for many years by the automobile industry. He devised the principle of the clincher tire. He worked out a number of varieties of tires and wheel rims, or felloes, in the shape of "metal troughs with edges inclined toward each other." Some of the tires had definite beaded edges but did not use reinforcing wires or bands of metal.

The Bartlett tire as first designed—with its thickened, slightly elastic edges made generally of hard rubber—was not in itself a true clincher. This initial construction proved not to be wholly practical, so each tire edge was reshaped into the form of a continuous hook. Rim flanges were modified to provide a shape this hook could engage. Air pressure locked together the tire hooks and rim hooks. This tire with its hooked edges or "clenches" (clinches) was called the "clincher" (Figure 15). Its rim, for a time known as the "Wedgewood" in England, eventually became the "clincher rim." The clincher tire also has been called the "beaded-edge" tire as distinguished from the "wired-on" or "Dunlop" type.

The Bartlett patent became the property of the North British Rubber Company. In 1903, it was acquired by the Dunlop Company for a purchase price reported to have been £120,000.

On the same day that Bartlett was issued a United States patent on his clincher idea, two other inventors obtained patents that helped outline the progress of tire development. E. R. DeWolfe, of New York City, molded in the base of the outer cover of his tire flat plates of "thin spring metal having beaded wire edges." These were sprung under the inward-curving edges of the wheel rim to hold the tire in place.

Thomas B. Jeffery, of Illinois, was issued a patent in 1891 on a tire having hooked edges engaging matching hook-shaped rim flanges. He received another patent in 1892 on a method of attaching bicycle tires to rims by means of separate hooks. The tire casing was slit open around its inner circumference so the tube could be inserted. Then, at intervals

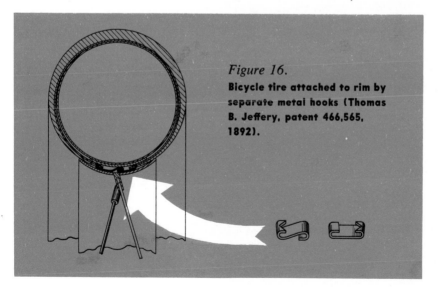

Figure 16.
Bicycle tire attached to rim by separate metal hooks (Thomas B. Jeffery, patent 466,565, 1892).

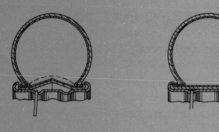

Figure 17.
Early tire showing "exterior projecting beads or spurs" (Thomas B. Jeffery, patent 466,789).

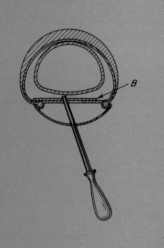

Figure 18.
Tire-fastening method patented in 1892 by A. T. Brown. A band of metal (B) fitting around the rim was moved sideways by a tool, to lock tire beads on their seats (U.S. patent 474,589).

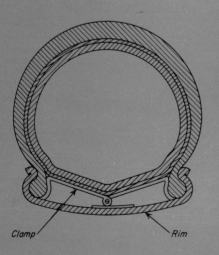

Figure 19.
Bead-locking arrangement patented by G. F. Stillman in 1893. Pressure of air in the tube forced the hingelike clamp against the beads (U.S. patent 495,277).

around the casing edges, holes were cut to receive hooks whose other ends engaged the inward-turned edges of the wheel rim, or felloe (Figure 16). A week later (January 12, 1892), Jeffery was granted another patent on a tire idea that became of considerable importance. Incorporated in the base of the tire were "exterior projecting beads or spurs" which, to hold the tire in place, were engaged by inward-curving rim flanges (Figure 17). Thus, at this early date in the story of pneumatic tires, the word "bead" was coming into use, along with the development of the clincher-tire idea.

During this period, inventive activity directed toward the perfection of methods of holding a tire on a wheel must have been considerable, for a number of other patents were issued on many phases of tire and rim construction and mounting. Among these were the following: To Alexander T. Brown, Syracuse, New York—a tire having enlarged or beaded edges fitting concave seats near the edges of the rim. Each tire edge was locked in place by a metal band encircling the central portion of the rim, the band being movable so it could be shifted sidewise by a pry bar until its edge overlapped the bead (Figure 18). To Alexander Straus, New York City—a tire whose outer casing had canvas or linen edges formed into hollow tubes through which were run wires or bands to hold it on the rim. To G. F. Stillman, Syracuse, New York—a method of locking beaded tire edges to the inward-curved flanges of the rim by means of sectional grip plates which, upon being straightened by pressure of the inflated tube, pressed the beads into the rim grooves (Figure 19).

DUNLOP'S WELCH-TYPE TIRE

THE CHARLES KINGSTON WELCH patent of 1890 for a "wired tire" became the property of the company that had been formed to manufacture Dunlop's tire. The Welch-type cycle tire consisted of an inner tube and an outer casing whose edges were formed into beads through which ran steel wires. At first, each tire bead was reinforced by a single steel wire 0.128 inch in diameter; later, several convolutions of finer wire were used. Ends were united by a scarfed and brazed joint over which a steel sleeve was sweated. This kind of joint continued in use in Dunlop cycle tires until 1935, at which time it was superseded by an electrically welded joint provided with a soldered sleeve. The Welch tires were used on "Westwood" rims, which were a hollow-center design very much like the drop-center kind in universal use today. The circumference of a rim at the edges or flanges was greater than the circumference of the tire beads, but at the center the rim circumference was less than that of the beads. To remove a tire from such a rim after the tube had been deflated, the beads were squeezed toward each other along one section until they could be pushed down into the hollow center of the rim. Then the opposite portion of the tire could be pulled over the rim flanges. To install a tire on a rim, the operation was reversed. Thus Welch and Dunlop used the principle of the drop-center rim long before it became the universal type it is today.

The single wire used so stiffened the beads that it was very difficult to install or remove a tire. So the single large wire was abandoned in favor of a bead-grommet made by twisting together three wires of smaller diameter. In the early days, wire suitable for the Dunlop-Welch tire beads was not easy to obtain, especially by persons who wanted to make tires "outside" of the Welch patent. So there developed a brisk market for worn-out Dunlop cycle tires. The wire bead reinforcements would be ripped out, and new tires built on them. The company, to discourage such activities, itself became a buyer of old tires. At one time the cyclist could get as much as a half crown for each of his worn-out casings.

The Welch patent covering the use of wire and similar reinforcements in tire beads was the center of many legal battles. These ended only when the patent expired and was fittingly burned at a dinner ceremony held by the Dunlop organization.

Not every owner of a bicycle equipped with Dunlop-Welch tires appreciated this ingenious arrangement for removing the tire from its rim. John Gammeter, of Akron, Ohio, one of the most prolific inventors in the rubber industry, recalls his first experience with such tires. It was around 1892, when he was about 16 years old, that he saw his first pneumatic tire. It was a single-tube type made of red rubber and was cemented to the crescent-shaped rim of a Victor bicycle wheel. About a year later he acquired a Premier bicycle having Dunlop tires containing wire beads. One day his front tire went flat and he took the wheel to a friend who ran a machine shop to have it repaired. But neither Gammeter nor the shop owner had the slightest idea how to remove the tire from the rim. They knew or discovered that the tire-casing edges contained strong steel wires, but they were unsuccessful in trying to force these edges over the rim flange. Finally they decided that the only way to get the thing off was to cut the bead wires. This they did, and were able to stretch the rubber enough to free the tire from the wheel.

Then they discovered the secret of getting the tire off the rim in the manner the manufacturer had intended: if they merely had squeezed the beads together so the tire could drop into the hollow center of the rim, they could have pulled it off without cutting the wires. Now they had another problem to solve: how to join the bead-wire ends again after the puncture had been repaired. They finally succeeded in coupling together the cut ends of the wires. Gammeter believes that this was the first Dunlop tire ever seen in Akron. In spite of his troubles with it, he became convinced that its design was good; and he says that later, during the clincher-tire era, he tried, but unsuccessfuly, to have development directed toward this type of construction wherein a wire-reinforced bead is used. But the clincher idea was firmly established, and the time for it to be replaced had not yet come.

The Dunlop-Welch tire for bicycles was sold in the United States, and license to manufacture it in this country was issued in 1896. This tire eventually was developed into a type suitable for use on automobiles.

TIRES WITH AND WITHOUT WIRE

*I*T IS DIFFICULT to say precisely when wire as a means of holding a tire on a rim first was used. While the Dunlop Company is said to have been the first to employ wire-reinforced beads extensively, wire in a tire was no novelty when Dr. Dunlop made the first set of pneumatics for his son's tricycle. But up to that time, the wire had been confined to solid and cushion tires, as already recounted.

Up to about 1895, all the improvements in solid and pneumatic tires, including the introduction and development of wire reinforcements in beads and elsewhere in the tire structure, were confined to cycle, carriage, and similar types of tires. One of the biggest headaches was the basic matter of keeping the tires on their wheels, or at least keeping them from creeping around the rims. For instance, the rubber tires on carriages in negotiating the rough roads and streets of the day, were subjected to great punishment and to distortions and stresses of many varieties. And so it is understandable that a tire occasionally would creep around its groove in the wheel felloe or rim, might stretch enough to pop out of the groove entirely, and otherwise could become a source of much annoyance, trouble, and even danger. It was to prevent such stretching, creeping, and other undesirable activities that steel wire, metal bands, and other inextensible reinforcements were added.

When the automobile came along, tires were waiting for it, but they were basically cycle and carriage tires, some solid or cushion, some pneumatic. It is reported that the first regular use of pneumatic tires on an automobile was in France around 1895.

It soon became apparent that the cycle tires of the day were not very well suited to automobile use. Greater weight to be supported, higher speeds, and more all-round punishment called for sturdier tires. Solid and cushion types were used widely, especially on commercial vehicles— even up to and beyond World War I. Pneumatic tires were at first confined mostly to passenger cars. Wire as a reinforcement continued to be a part of solid tires. In pneumatic types, wire was used in nonextensible beads in such tires as the Dunlop-Welch; but the clincher era was built around tires having stretchable beads containing no wire or other metal reinforcement. Then, as the clincher began to give way to the straight-side tire and eventually was superseded by it, wire came back into its own and today is used in virtually every pneumatic tire made.

The reasons why the clincher tire was able to nose out the superior wired-on type developed by Dunlop and Welch seem to have been legal rather than technical. For a while, the wire-bead and extensible-bead or clincher tires were used chiefly on cycle wheels. The wire-bead construction was restricted, by patents, to Great Britain; but owners of the rights to clincher construction licensed manufacturers in other countries to use the clincher principle. When the automobile, with its need for larger, more rugged tires, began to flourish, various legal restrictions were set up in Great Britain which are said to have acted as barriers to its development—such as regulations imposing very low speed limits and requiring that an automobile must be preceded by someone carrying a red flag. So on the Continent, especially in France, automobile development proceeded much more rapidly. But in France, no manufacturer was licensed to make wire-bead tires. So tire-making efforts were concentrated on the clincher tire, which was not restricted to Great Britain. By the time British restrictions on automobiles were eased, the clincher tire had become so firmly established that it was able to stay in first place for many years on a world-wide basis. Eventually the Welch patent expired, and the wire-bead and clincher principles could compete at a strictly engineering level. In the United States, around 1905, the wire-bead or straight-sidewall tire began to push the clincher type out of the picture. It took a lot of pushing, extending over a good many years, before the clincher habit had become practically nonexistent. In fact, clincher tires are still being made, but only in insignificant numbers for replacement purposes.

The development of the pneumatic tire and the wire in it is closely tied to the development of the rim, and a review of rim history will throw further light on tire and bead progress.

PATENTS MENTIONED IN CHAPTER 2

Inventor	U.S.	British	Year
Ahlborn, George	456,751		1891
Bartlett, William E.		11,900	1889
		16,348	1890
		16,783	1890
	448,793		1891
	466,532		1892
Brown, Alexander T.	474,589		1892
Brown and Stillman	488,494		1892
Cheever, J. H.	86,504		1869
DeWolfe, E. R.	466,556		1892
Dunlop, John Boyd		10,607	1888
		4,116	1889
Greene, J. A.	91,435		1869
	169,100		1875
Ham, Daniel	92,606		1869
Harris, F. H.	371,580		1887
Jefferies and Grant	449,650		1891
Jeffery, Thomas B.	383,129		1888
	454,115		1891
	466,565		1892
	466,789		1892
Powell, A. G.	452,649		1891
Southland and Klauser	420,610		1890
Stillman, G. F.	495,277		1893
Straus, Alexander	474,423		1892
Thomas, Amos W.	399,354		1889
Thomson, Robert W.		10,990	1845
	5,104		1847
Welch, Charles Kingston		14,563	1890
	512,594		1894

CHAPTER 3 § THE STORY OF RIMS

THE RIM on which a pneumatic tire is mounted can trace its ancestry directly to what is probably man's oldest mechanical invention, the wheel. It has acted either as an intermediate ring between tire and wheel felloe or as the felloe itself, the felloe, or "felly" as the old-timers said, being the outer hoop of the wheel, to which are attached the outermost ends of the spokes. At one time the wheel rim was itself a tire: in the days before rubber tires, the felloe of a wagon, buggy, or other vehicle wheel was encircled by a steel band or tire. Then, almost without changing its form, this band was used as a rubber-tire support, and thereby it became a rim.

RIM SHAPES

THE STEEL rims on which the early solid and cushion rubber tires were mounted were generally shaped to provide a circumferential channel in which the tire was placed. The side flanges of this channel were intended to prevent the tire from shifting laterally. They did not always do this, a fact that ultimately exerted influence in the development of wire reinforcements and beads. The early tire rims, grooved either by machining them or by the less costly process of bending flat strips into channels, had a multitude of cross-sectional shapes. There were simple U shapes, dovetail grooves, rims with inward-curving sides very much like the later clincher types, rectangular channels, curved-bottom ones, and so on. At least one inventor reversed things by putting the channel in the rubber tire, fitting it over a plain rim of rectangular section, and holding it there with lacings (U.S. patent 92,606).

Later it was found more convenient to have the channeled rim separable from the wheel so it could be slid on or off the wheel felloe or fixed rim.

When Robert William Thomson patented the first pneumatic tire in 1845, he described it, in one form, as being mounted on the flat face of the wheel and secured by means of bolts passing through the casing of the tire, inward through the felloe, and terminating in nuts tightened against the inner circumference of the felloe. In describing his invention, Thomson suggested that his "hollow belt" be mounted on a felloe much broader than those customarily used on vehicle wheels of comparable size. In fact, his tires as designed for common passenger carriages were 4 to 5 inches in diameter and were inflated so they held the wheel 2½ to 3 inches above the ground.

DUNLOP'S WHEEL

When John Boyd Dunlop, almost a half century later, revived the pneumatic-tire idea, he started with a wheel even simpler than Thomson's. It was nothing more than a 15-inch wooden disk. His pneumatic tire was a tube made of $\frac{1}{32}$-inch sheet rubber covered with linen obtained—as Dr. Dunlop explained before a Society of Automotive Engineers meeting in the United States in 1913—from a remnant of a woman's dress. The tire was fastened around the periphery of this disk by nailing through the linen, flaps probably having been provided for that purpose. Rubber tubing of the type used on children's feeding bottles was employed for the air-supply tube. The reason that Dr. Dunlop's first pneumatic-shod wheel was so simple is that he employed it, not as an element on a vehicle, but as a device for testing the relative performances of pneumatic and solid tires while rolling it like a hoop over the ground. When

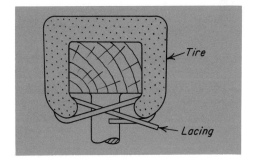

Figure 1.

One of the simplest rim arrangements consisted of a wooden wheel felloe around which was laced a channel-shaped solid-rubber tire. It was designed for carriages and cycles (Daniel Ham, patent 92,606, 1869).

the air-filled tire outperformed the solid one with respect to distance traveled before falling over and ease and speed of negotiating rough ground, he was ready for more practical trials.

Dr. Dunlop fashioned a set of pneumatic tires for his son's tricycle—probably the vehicle that had proved to be so jarring when negotiating the paving blocks of Belfast streets. Before he could put these tires into use, the Doctor had to have something suitable on which to mount them. So he constructed wheels by bending thin strips of wood into ring-shaped felloes, and attaching spokes. The faces of these felloes were flat, like those on most vehicles of the day. He provided the tires with canvas flaps to help in cementing and otherwise fastening them to the wheels. In place and inflated, this type of tire had a cross section that was rounded except where it flattened against the rim face. A rubber valve, whose stem extended through a hole in the wheel felloe (just like present-day ones), permitted air to flow into the tire but not out. A patent drawing of an early Dunlop tire (U.S. patent 453,550) shows the rim wrapped with canvas over which was placed a layer of sheet rubber. A canvas strip extending part way around the sidewalls between the inner tube and the cover was brought over the rim, and finally the cover edges (corresponding to beaded edges of later tires) were brought around the rim edges and part way toward the center, and cemented.

RIMS FOR FIRST WIRE-BEAD TIRES

*I*N 1890 Charles Kingston Welch put wire bead reinforcement in tires, and this immediately changed the rim picture. Welch mounted his tire on a metal rim that had, near each edge, a groove shaped to receive the beads (see page 20). In the United States, a parallel development of the wire-bead tire was the subject of a patent issued to A. T. Brown and

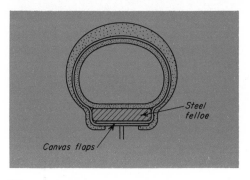

Figure 2.

Early pneumatic tire designed by Dr. Dunlop. The casing was fastened to a steel rim by canvas flaps cemented under steel felloe (U.S. patent 453,550).

G. F. Stillman (see page 20). The rim suggested by Brown and Stillman was, like the Welch design, of curved cross section, and was of less circumference at the center than at the edges. Near these edges the rim, made of steel sheet or plate, was shaped to provide recesses or seats for the beaded edges of the tire. It is noteworthy that, in form, both the Welch and the Brown-Stillman rims were very much alike and that they were prototypes of present-day drop-center rims. Subsequent developments indicated that the two inventions were made independently of each other.

The rim design suggested by Welch was used with the tire produced by Dunlop under the Welch patent. The edges of this hollow- or depressed-center steel rim were formed into tubes so shaped and positioned as to provide channels in which the beaded edges of the tire rested. To remove a deflated tire, the beads were squeezed together and forced into the depressed rim center, after which the opposite side of the tire could be pulled over the rim edge. Since the circumference of the tire at the beads was less than the circumference of the rim at its edges (flanges), this was the only way the tire could be removed—for the wire-reinforced beads were not extensible. Virtually the same arrangement of "buttonholing" is in use today in the form of the drop-center automobile rim. Of course, when installing a tire on such a rim, the procedure is the reverse of that used in removing it.

Later the Welch-type cycle tire produced by Dunlop was modified so it could be used on automobile wheels. A typical form of the rim used with it was shown in the *India Rubber World* for January 1, 1904, page 130. In cross section the rim was a flat, hollow rectangle with curved-bottom grooves on its outer face near the edges, which received steel rings whose ends were joined by turnbuckles. These rings rested against the wire-reinforced beaded edges of the tire casing, forming a seat for them and preventing the beads from being pushed off the rim by inflation pressure. The turnbuckles were turned by rods, heavy nails, or similar tools inserted into radial holes. It is said that a set of tires to fit these rims might cost nearly $250.

CLINCHER-TIRE RIMS

$\mathcal{T}$HE CLINCHER-TIRE rim apparently was the outgrowth largely of the work of two inventors. In Edinburgh, Scotland, William Erskine Bartlett, beginning in 1890, proposed a number of arrangements of cushion and pneumatic tires and mounts. One of these mounts was described as "a rim or metal tyre of a trough section the sides of the trough inclining towards each other." That is, the rim flanges were turned inward instead of being curved outward as were the Welch rim flanges. These inclining, or dovetail, rim edges formed channels in which the thickened edges of the tire rested. Bartlett's tires consisted of endless bands of rubber wider than the wheel rim. When the edges of such a band were forced together so they could enter the rim channels, the rubber was arched into a tire that was roughly U-shaped. Later the early Bartlett design was modified to provide hook-shaped edges matching inward-curving rim flanges.

While Bartlett was devising his tires and rims, Thomas B. Jeffery in the United States was working along similar lines.

In time, the Bartlett and Jeffery clincher patents became the subject of litigation in England and the United States. Eventually, in the interests of peace, the two inventions entered upon a sort of marriage. From this union came the clincher tire and rim ultimately adopted on a world-wide scale. There has been some discussion to the effect that Bartlett did not actually have in mind the clincher rim, while Jeffery did. Bartlett's patent drawings show no hooks such as characterized later clincher arrangements; Jeffery's drawings do. The first Bartlett tires are said to have been unsatisfactory and to have been redesigned to incorporate hooked edges. The rims suggested by both Jeffery and Bartlett have depressed centers, but this detail seems to have been considered of no importance in installing or removing a tire. The Jeffery tire was developed into the Gormully and Jeffery clincher tire for bicycles and was commonly known as the "G & J." It had double bead hooks and fitted matching grooves in a wooden rim. This tire was used on Rambler bicycles.

The basic clincher rim was simplicity itself, but in order to be workable, it had to be used with tires whose beads were designed for it. The rim had a flat base, and its edges curved inward to form continuous recesses, one on each side, for the beads to slide under. Outward pressure of the inner tube forced the beads apart. This action served to keep them under the curved rim edges, thereby holding the tire on the wheel. In cross section, the rim shape resembled somewhat that assumed by the talons of an eagle when it is grasping its prey: the inward-curving flanges of the clincher rim grasped the tire beads which were shaped to fit under them.

Here was a simple arrangement: a one-piece rim whose inwardly curving edges grasped the tire. But in order to get the tire on and off the rim, the beads had to be stretched enough to slip over the flanged edges. The beads were built up of fabric and rubber in such a way that they provided a strong, relatively rigid foundation for the tire as long as they were hooked in the clincher-rim grooves. But when unhooked, they could be stretched enough, with the aid of suitable pry bars and other tools, to let them slip over the rim flange.

The first clincher tires were used on bicycles and were generally satisfactory because tires and rims were relatively small (compared with later automotive types) and were easy to handle. Then came the automobile; and because of its greater loads and speeds, tires had to become larger, heavier, stronger, and tougher. Some single-tube automobile tires were made (simple inflated rubber rings mounted on rims of concave section), and the wire-bead tire was already known. But largely because of involved legal and legislative conditions (see page 28), it was the clincher tire that was adopted for the earliest motor cars and which managed to carry virtually all of the automotive burden until about 1905. Then other ideas began to encroach upon its monopoly. Gradually the clincher gave way to the straight-sidewall idea until, by 1914, the straight-side tire was in general use, and by 1916 about the only new cars using clinchers were Fords. In the late 1920's, the clincher tire had retired from the new-car picture, although clinchers had to be made as late as World War II for clincher rims still in general use; and at least two rubber companies continue to make such tires largely as a favor to the antique-auto fans.

EARLY TIRE TROUBLES

$\mathcal{T}$HE FIRST clincher rims were mounted directly on the wooden wheel felloes; that is, the felloe and clincher rim were permanent assemblies. Whenever a motorist got a flat tire, he had to jack up the wheel, pry the tire and tube off the wheel, either repair the damage or get out a fresh tube and casing, and then pry and otherwise force the tire back on the wheel. Finally, he had to reinflate the tire with a hand pump. It was generally agreed among motorists of the day that this was hard, distasteful work, especially in bad weather and on a muddy road.

As loads increased and tire sizes became greater, the difficulties of removing and replacing clincher tires multiplied. Tires would creep around the rims; chafing, cutting, and breaking of the casing at the bead were not uncommon. So beads were made stronger and heavier, and therefore more difficult for the motorist to stretch over a clincher rim. The operation of putting a clincher tire on a rim or removing it was likely to be tough on the inner tube. Tubes made of red rubber were introduced so the tire changer could distinguish tube from tire casing and therefore be less likely to pinch the tube between the tire tool and rim.

DETACHABLE-FLANGE RIMS

*T*HE SIMPLE one-piece clincher rim began to undergo a change. It was split into two parts, one being a flange that could be unfastened and removed. No longer must the tire be stretched over a rim flange of greater diameter than the beaded edges. Once the flange had been removed, the tire and its deflated tube could be slipped on or off the rim by straight, relatively easy pulling or pushing. Now the beads could be made more rugged to withstand increased punishment, could even be reinforced with wire, for they no longer had to be stretchable.

Numerous types of detachable rims were designed, and many kinds of fastening devices used. The rim flange, for instance, might be held in place by a retaining ring tightened with a turnbuckle arrangement. The retaining member might be simply a split ring that was snapped into or pried out of its groove, flange and ring being shaped so that the ring was locked in position when the tire was inflated. Or the flange itself might be a split ring sprung into or out of its groove in the main part of the rim.

DEMOUNTABLE RIMS

*B*Y CONSTRUCTING the clincher rim with a removable flange (or two removable flanges), manufacturers had made it easier for the motorist to get a tire on or off its wheel. But still the job had to be done on the road, wherever and in whatever weather the tire failed. In France, where automobile racing had become a popular sport, rapid changing of tires assumed considerable importance; and to save valuable seconds in races, demountable rims were introduced. These were made so they could be slipped with comparative ease and speed on or off the wheel felloes. Before long, the demountable idea was made available to the everyday motorist.

Now he could carry a spare tire and tube already mounted and inflated, and all he had to do when a tire failed was remove the deflated assembly of tire, tube, and rim from the wheel and install another rim bearing a tire already inflated. The change could be made in much less time than when the tire had to be taken off the rim, and repairs to the damaged tire could be carried out at any time after the trip had been completed. While it was feasible to make a demountable rim in the form of a simple one-piece clincher type—and this was done—the detachable-flange feature continued to grow in popularity because, whether or not the rim was on a wheel, it made the tire easier to handle.

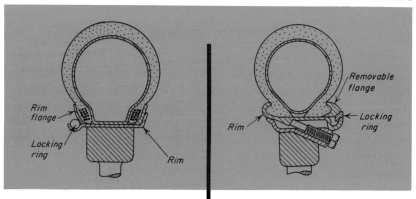

Figure 3.

Detachable-flange rim arrangement patented by Scott in 1906. Removable flange was held in place by locking-ring (patent 816,884).

Figure 4.

Detachable-flange, demountable rim designed by John R. Gammeter in 1914. Locking ring held removable flange in place (patent 1,088,656).

SPLIT CLINCHER RIMS

A CLINCHER-RIM development which had some influence on bead design was the splitting of the rim by a transverse cut, or the making of the rim in two sections hinged together at one joint and provided with a locking device at the other. To remove a tire from a split rim, the rim joint was unlocked and one of the disengaged ends was sprung inward toward the center; special tools, some of them operating somewhat like a screw-type automobile jack, were sold for this purpose. The inward springing of the rim, accompanied by disengagement of the beads from the flanges, reduced its diameter so the tire could be slipped off. In mounting a tire on a rim, the reverse operation was equally easy. Because it was not necessary to stretch the beads, they could be made inextensible, as with wire reinforcements—just as a quick-detachable clincher rim of the removable-flange type made it possible to use wire-bead clincher tires.

And so there came into the automobile picture the detachable-demountable rim, which was one having a detachable flange so the tire could be removed easily from it and just as easily replaced, and which itself was removable from the wheel. A variation was the split demountable rim.

37

THE STRAIGHT-SIDEWALL TIRE

*B*UT IN spite of such modifications as detachable flanges and reinforced beads, the clincher tire was beginning to lose its monopoly. From an engineering standpoint, it never was considered the most desirable type. The true clincher automobile tire on a one-piece rim was not easy to remove or replace, even in the relatively small 3- and 3½-inch sizes. The bigger the tire, the more difficult would be the crowbar work involved in mounting or removing it; and bigger tires were becoming a necessity. The solution was found in the straight-sidewall tire, a variety first made popular on bicycles by Dunlop but hampered by patent and legislative restrictions which enabled the clincher to outdistance it in European automobile applications. This straight-side tire was held in place on the rim by wire bead reinforcements; and since the clincher hooks were not needed, the sides of the tire in the region of the beads could be made straight instead of being curved into hooks—hence the term "straight-sidewall," "straight-side," or, simply, "s.s."

The Goodyear Tire and Rubber Company and Firestone Tire and Rubber Company have been credited with taking the initiative in pushing the straight-side tire idea until it was accepted by motor car manufacturers and car owners. As the story with respect to Goodyear goes, Paul W. Litchfield, around 1904, became dissatisfied with the clincher tire and with the variety of unwieldy flanges and locking devices being used to make the clincher stay properly on its rim when running and come off with reasonable ease when deflated. Litchfield was superintendent of the company (which had been founded by F. A. Seiberling), and one of his jobs was to improve the company's tires. During the time when he was wrestling with the idea of developing something that would be better than the clincher tire, a colorful inventor named Charles S. Scott, but commonly called "Nip," from Cadiz, Ohio, would stop occa-

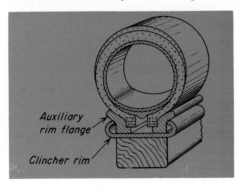

Auxiliary
rim flange

Clincher rim

Figure 5.

For his tire having braided-wire bead reinforcements, C. S. Scott devised a rim arrangement whereby the straight-side tire could be mounted on a clincher rim. He accomplished this by means of auxiliary rim flanges made of rubber or other semielastic material (patent 770,611).

sionally to visit him and Seiberling. One day Nip, lugging a burlap bag, appeared. The contents of that bag, which he dumped on Seiberling's desk, proved to be the key to the company's tire problem of that moment.

Nip Scott, whose inventiveness carried him into many fields, had come across the idea of braiding wire into a flat tape. He is said to have first become interested in wire braid for its possible use in bedsprings but found it too costly for that purpose. Then he got the idea of using the braided-steel ribbon as a reinforcement in pneumatic tire beads; and he designed a tire that had a straight side and could be used on a clincher or nonclincher rim (U.S. patent 770,611, 1904). The wire braid was sufficiently inextensible to hold the tire securely on its rim; yet it possessed sufficient flexibility to simplify handling during manufacture, and, after vulcanization of the rubber, to withstand road shock and stress well and to permit the tire to be easily removed or replaced.

And so the straight-side cycle tire of Brown, Stillman, Welch, and Dunlop was reborn for the motor car. It was held on the rim, not by hooked edges and flanges, but by the tensile strength of the wire-braid reinforcement in the beads; and it was prevented from shifting laterally by the outward-flaring rim flanges. The Goodyear company set out to make its new straight-side tire popular, a process that is said to have encountered a lot of resistance and to have required considerable time.

The Firestone phase of the straight-side story seems to have gotten under way at about the same time as that of Goodyear. In 1904, Harvey Firestone's application to make clincher tires was rejected by the interests that controlled clincher patents. So he and an engineer began a search for a way to omit the clincher construction and yet produce a workable pneumatic tire. A nonclincher bead reinforced by steel wire was selected, the wire being in the form of a cable. A method of securing the tire to the rim by means of bolts and metal plates was worked out. The new straight-side tire was test-run in 1905, and soon was offered for sale.

REVERSIBLE FLANGES

*A*T ABOUT this point in the romance of tires and rims, the motorist had a choice to make: either a clincher tire fitting one kind of rim or a straight-side tire fitting another. But it did not take manufacturers long to come up with a solution. The Firestone Tire and Rubber Company pioneered in turning out rims that had two interchangeable sets of detachable flanges. One set was shaped to fit clincher beads, the other to provide proper seats for straight-side beads. In some cases one pair of flanges could be used for either bead shape, being changed from one type to the other simply by reversing their positions on the rim base. And motorists who had clincher rims they were reluctant to discard were not forgotten: various attachments to enable straight-side tires to be mounted on clincher rims were brought out. In fact, the Nip Scott patent describing his wire-braid bead reinforcement illustrated a way of mounting such a bead on a clincher rim, with the aid of two auxiliary flange rings made of rubber or other material.

At one period in the development of tires, the rims had become really complicated pieces of equipment. A quick-detachable demountable rim capable of supporting either a clincher or a straight-side tire involved, of necessity, quite a few parts. The rim itself consisted of a base, a pair of removable flanges, locking rings, and other devices of various degrees of complication. Then the rim had to be held on the wheel felloe by a further complexity of lugs, restraining rings, blocks to prevent the rim from slipping around the felloe, and so on. All this was quite in contrast with the simple one-piece clincher rim. But that the detachable and demountable features were sound is indicated by the fact that, today, truck tires are mounted on rims having much the same construction, although the clincher portion has not survived.

EXAMPLES OF RIMS

S*imple Clincher.* In its simplest form, the clincher rim consisted of a one-piece channeled ring rolled cold from flat hot-rolled steel stock. The following specifications for open-hearth steel used in Goodyear clincher rims are typical: carbon, 0.012 to 0.020 per cent; sulfur, not over 0.050 per cent; phosphorus, not over 0.050 per cent; manganese, 0.035 to

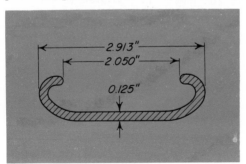

Figure 6.

Cross section of one-piece clincher rim for 3½-inch tire. Dimensions are those in use in 1916. Special 30- by 3½-inch clincher rims for Ford cars were made to 0.125-inch gauge.

0.040 per cent. The rim was mounted directly on the wheel felloe, which, in the early days, was generally made of wood. When wire-spoke wheels came into popularity, spokes were attached directly to the rim.

Demountable Clincher. When the demountable idea was adopted for clincher rims, an additional band was shrunk on the wooden felloe. This was called the inner or felloe band. On a typical wheel installation (Firestone), it was flat over the area in contact with the felloe and for a ⅛-inch projection in front, and curved outward along the rear edge to form a seat matching the contour of the clincher rim. The rim and inner band were separated ³⁄₁₆ inch except along this seat. Bolts spaced around the wheel forced wedge-shaped lugs between the inner band and front portion of the rim, the outer surface of each lug being shaped to fit the contour of the rim.

Detachable-flange Rims. The simplest detachable-flange rim consisted of either a clincher or straight-side tire rim mounted directly on a wooden wheel felloe or supported by wire spokes directly attached, the spoke ends being contained in channels or countersunk to present a smooth rim surface. The outer flange of the rim was a separate unit and was removed before the deflated tire was pulled off or replaced. In a typical construction (Goodyear), the flange was a split ring resting in a seat formed by rolling a channel around the edge of the rim base. When the flange was snapped into position, its ends were separated about ¹⁄₁₆ inch, and one end was notched so a tool could be inserted for prying it loose. The flange could be shaped so that, turned one way, it would be usable on a clincher-tire rim; turned the other, on a straight-side rim.

Quick-detachable Demountable Rims (commonly known as the "Q.D." demountable). By combining the detachable-flange and demountable-rim features, an automobile wheel of just about maximum complexity was produced. There were three general kinds of detachable-demountable rims:

1. The demountable clincher rim with one detachable flange.
2. The demountable straight-side rim with one detachable flange. Sometimes the flange was designed so it could be used with either type.
3. A "universal" demountable rim having two detachable flanges which could be reversed to provide properly shaped seats for either clincher or straight-side beads.

Numerous schemes were worked out for locking the flange on the rim and for fastening the rim on the wheel. The inner, or back, flange of the

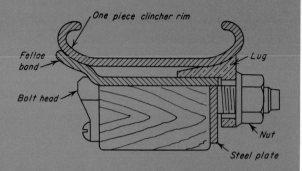

One piece clincher rim

Felloe band

Bolt head

Lug

Nut

Steel plate

Figure 7.

A typical demountable clincher rim mounted on a wooden wheel. Each rim lug bolt had a special head, which was prevented from turning by a wood screw extending through a hole and into the felloe.

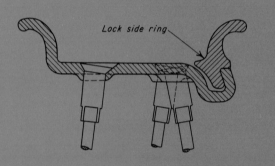

Lock side ring

Figure 8.

Passenger-car detachable-flange rim on wire wheel. Detachable flange is in form of locking side ring which can be used with either a clincher or straight-side tire.

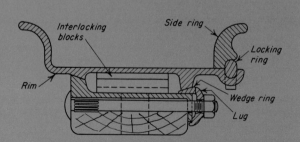

Interlocking blocks

Side ring

Locking ring

Rim

Wedge ring

Lug

Figure 9.

A 44- by 10-inch demountable truck-tire rim (1920). Interlocking blocks on rim and felloe prevented rim from slipping around wheel in heavy pulls. This was a flat-base rim, there being no angled bead seats as in many later rims. Truck rims of similar design are in use today.

universal type rested against the outward-flared edge of the rim. The outer, or front, flange might rest in a channel and require no other locking mechanism, since the pressure of the tire bead would hold it there; or it might be held in place by an additional locking ring resting in a channel rolled into the rim base near the front (outer) edge.

Whatever the type of locking device, it was a general practice to make the rim and inner ring on which it rested of such cross-sectional shape that the mechanical contact between these two parts and between them and any intermediate locking rings or lugs was kept relatively small. Actually, contact was restricted to two narrow bands extending around the circumference near the inner-ring edges. By not allowing the rim and felloe band to be in complete contact, difficulties arising from rusting were lessened; that is, it was easier to break loose a rusted rim if it touched the felloe band only along two narrow strips than if it had been in contact over the entire width of the band.

By the time the clincher tire was about ready to be retired completely from its place of popularity, straight-side tires on detachable rims had become standard equipment. While the demountable-rim feature had

Figure 10.

Quick-detachable tire on a demountable rim (1909). Flange was locked in place by a split ring. Rim was locked on felloe by wedging action.

Figure 11.

This rim was similar to the demountable clincher, but both flanges were detachable and reversible to accommodate either a clincher or straight-side tire.

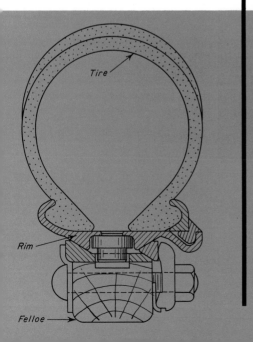

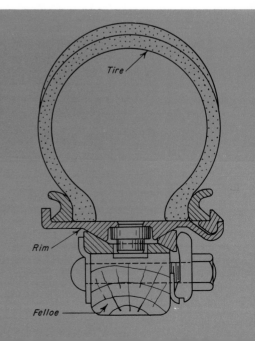

been generally accepted, a newer idea, also borrowed from automobile racing, was to make the entire wheel, instead of just the rim, demountable.

THE DROP-CENTER RIM

*T*o go back to the late 1800's for a moment, several inventors suggested rims with depressed centers. The Dunlop-Welch cycle tire, based on the Welch patent, was mounted on a hollow-center rim, the depressed portion serving as a space into which the tire beads of one section were forced so that the tire, in a generally diametrically opposite region, could be pulled over the rim flange. Thus the tire was removed or replaced by a "button-holing" operation. When this method was first tried with automobile tires, trouble was encountered because greater lateral stresses associated with automobile-wheel behavior sometimes would push the tire beads into the rim well when the car was in motion. This, of course, caused difficulties

Figure 12.

Dunlop light-motor tire on Dunlop-Welch depressed-center rim (1899). Introduced into the United States around 1924. This rim, initially manu-factured for one line of cars, was followed by a general adoption of the drop-center principle for American passenger cars.

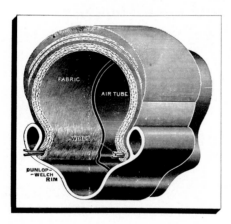

THREE NEW PATTERNS

of these celebrated pneumatic tyres (the first in 1888, and foremost ever since) are now perfected for **HEAVY MOTORS, LIGHT MOTORS,** and **MOTOR CYCLES** respectively.

This illustration depicts the section of the

DUNLOP LIGHT MOTOR TYRE.

Illustrated Price Lists now ready.

The Dunlop Pneumatic Tyre Co., Ltd.,

ALMA STREET, COVENTRY.

and, no doubt, sometimes disaster. The development of the removable-flange rim having a flat base instead of a hollow one eliminated the hollow-center hazard in the early automobile tires.

But the depressed-center rim idea was not abandoned. While automobile tires were being mounted on clincher and straight-side rims having flat bases, bicycle and motorcycle rims shaped substantially the same as the early Dunlop-Welch rim were continuing in use. Then, around 1924, there was brought to this country from England, primarily for use on Ford cars, the English-type depressed-center balloon-tire rim. This was rolled from steel, its edges being shaped into tubular-section flanges, as shown in Figure 12.

By 1929 the hollow-center or depressed-center rim, better known in the United States as the drop-center, had been generally adopted for use on American passenger cars. Improved knowledge of bead construction and improved materials made it possible to construct a bead-rim combination that would withstand the rigors of modern motoring. No longer was it commonplace for the beads of deflated tires to pop down into the rim center while the car was in motion. A modification of the drop-center rim is the rolling of a hump or ridge around the rim between each bead and the rim well. This is said to reduce any tendency the beads might have to slip into the rim well in event of tire failure, thereby maintaining better stability of the deflated tire and better control while bringing the vehicle to a complete stop.

When the hollow-, depressed-, or drop-center rim was revived in the 1920's and engineers began to refine it for use on American cars, they encountered some difficulties. They had to develop tires and tubes that would give satisfactory performance with this kind of rim. A common fault at first was the chafing of the tube on the beads, in the absence of a flap. Tubes made extra-thick along the bead lines were tried, but this did not prove to be the ideal remedy. Finally the chafing troubles were overcome by fitting the tire more tightly to its rim. This stabilized the beads so that they could not rock; up to then, rocking beads had been the chief cause of tube damage in the drop-center assembly.

The drop-center rim was made an integral part of the wheel, which was demountable at the hub. This type of rim, once it was accepted as a practical development, forced the demountable rim out of the picture in the passenger-car field, although demountables still are used on commercial vehicles.

45

INCLINED BEAD SEATS

*U*P TO THE TIME the drop-center rim was adopted for American cars, tires were being made with beads to fit flat rims. Drop-center rims were made with cylindrical bead seats. Because of the use of low inflation pressures, there was a problem with respect to the seating of the beads securely on such cylindrical seats. The lower tire pressures were not sufficient to hold the beads tightly enough against the rim flanges. So the rim design was changed to provide tapered or inclined bead seats. Now when the bead was forced outward by inflation pressure, it was traveling uphill, and the resulting wedging action of the bead seats produced a sufficiently tight fit.

During this period, tire companies began to be plagued with loose treads on the passenger-car tires they made. This developed into a virtual epidemic. The cause of the trouble was found to be the drop-center rims on which the tires were being mounted. This kind of rim was of one-piece construction, so there were no cracks or joints through which entrapped air could escape; and there was an airtight fit between the tire casing and the rim. Air trapped when the tire was mounted would collect in the tire walls, build up pressure, and might eventually force the tread off. The remedy adopted in several plants was a simple one: with a slender awl, tiny holes were punched all the way through each new tire before it left the factory. This provided paths for the entrapped air to escape, thus preventing it from accumulating and blowing the tread loose. Some tire makers, instead of piercing the casing, depended on tiny grooves or ridges molded in the inner-tube surface to conduct entrapped air to the valve stem, where it could escape through the hole in the rim.

About 25 years after the drop-center rim migrated to the United States from England and began to supplant the quick-detachable demountable types, the over-all rim picture looks somewhat like this: In the United States, the drop-center rim is universally used on passenger cars and on some light trucks and other commercial vehicles. A semi-drop-center rim whose design permits larger brake drums is being used on some trucks. But typical of the truck-tire rims most widely used today are several varieties of quick-detachable ones offered by various manufacturers.

Truck Rim Types. These include the following rims, which for convenience have been grouped according to construction and arrangement of rings:

1. Two-piece rim combination consisting of a split base and a con-

tinuous side ring fitting in a groove at the outer edge of the rim base (Goodyear).

2. Two-piece rim having a continuous base and split side ring fitting in groove at outer edge of base (Goodyear, CWC).

3. Three-piece rim having a continuous rim base, a continuous outer side ring, and a split lock ring (Firestone, Goodyear, CWC).

4. Two-piece advanced-type rim consisting of a continuous base and a continuous side ring (Firestone).

5. Three-piece advanced-type rim consisting of a continuous base, continuous side ring, and split lock ring extending inward to form a 5-degree sloping bead seat (Firestone).

6. Three-piece advanced-type rim similar to No. 5 but with sloping bead seat on continuous side ring instead of on split locking ring (Kelsey-Hayes).

Some rim types are for use on disk wheels only.

The advanced-type rim, which is considered one of the latest steps in rim design, has sloping bead seats, the angle of slope being 5 degrees. For a number of years, The Firestone Tire and Rubber Company used a sloping seat on the inner side of its truck-tire rims. It was found that the beads which rested on such slopes were in better condition after long usage than those on the other (removable-flange) sides. This was because the inner bead of a tire, being tightly held by the wedging action of the bead seat and air pressure, could not wobble or rock as did the other bead, which rested against the removable outer ring and on a non-sloping seat. When rims for combat-type tires on military vehicles were needed, sloping bead seats on both sides were specified. Later, this slope feature was adopted for commercial-vehicle rims.

The largest pneumatic-tire rims made today are for use with earth-mover tires—those carrying huge dump trucks, scrapers, and other earth-moving equipment. Some of these rims weigh 800 pounds apiece. One form of earth-mover rim is of the semi-drop-center type and has two detachable flanges, and its bead seats are knurled to increase traction between tire and rim. One flange is held by a split locking ring. A variation is a five-piece assembly consisting of the rim base, two flanges, a lock ring, and a removable bead-seat band to support the outer bead of the tire.

In truck and similar commercial-vehicle operation, it is important that rims be used which do not contribute to bead damage or undue wear. This is because of the widespread practice of retreading truck tires. Unless its beads, as well as other parts of the carcass, remain in good condition, a tire cannot, with safety, have its useful life prolonged by the application of a new tread.

Solid-tire rims are still being manufactured for use with industrial-vehicle tires—factory trucks and so on. Such a rim is essentially a simple ring having side flanges to produce a channel for the tire, which is cured or vulcanized to the ring. The bottom of the channel is grooved, by coarse threading, to increase the area of contact between the rim metal and the rubber.

CORROSION OF RIMS

THROUGHOUT the history of pneumatic-tire rims, corrosion had been an important problem—and still is. The early quick-detachable and demountable rims evidently were a constant source of trouble because of corroding bolts, nuts, lugs, locking rings, and other parts. Between the felloe band shrunk over the wooden wheel, and the inside area of the rim, there existed an ideal pocket for the retention of water and dirt, and corrosion there was virtually unavoidable. By separating the rim and band except for narrow areas of contact, the total amount of metal surfaces likely to rust together was reduced, and the rim could be driven or pried off easily.

Another source of trouble has been corrosion of the rim under the tire beads. One of the best ways of preventing it is to make the beads tight fitting. Conversely, tight-fitting beads cannot be kept that way if the

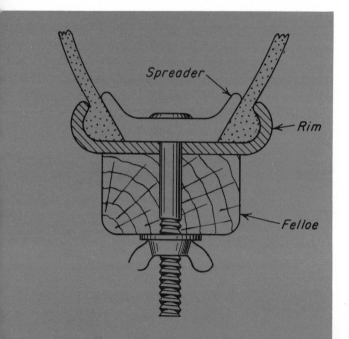

Figure 13.
In the early days, clincher tires often were locked to rims by spreaders secured with bolts and nuts. The valve-stem assembly also might serve as a spreader.

Figure 14.
These 36- x 4-inch Goodrich clincher tires of 1898, believed to have been the first double-tube automobile tires built in America, were locked on their rims by stay bolts and wing nuts.

rim or flange is permitted to corrode excessively along the bead line. In modern trucking practice, corrosion under the beads is an important item in maintenance. A typical heavy-duty truck tire is mounted on a rim having a removable side flange. This flange extends inward under the tire to form part or all of the bead seat and is tapered (e.g., 5 degrees) to make the beads seat tightly. In normal trucking operations, water may get into the rim and work its way between beads and seats, causing rusting of the latter. It is claimed that the water usually enters through the valve-stem hole in the rim. Materials such as rubber putty have been suggested for sealing around the valve stem to keep water out; but in practice, the people who change truck tires seem disinclined to replace the putty each time a tire has been removed and remounted. So water still gets into rims, and corrosion results.

This corrosion, if not controlled, can cause two kinds of damage: (1) It may eat away the bead seat until the effective circumference of the rim along the beads is reduced, and the tire no longer fits tightly. The resultant slipping and rocking at the beads can lead to trouble. (2) Some side rings have been made so thin that, along the bead seat, corrosion would cause a ring to lose its rigidity and become distorted, perhaps resulting ultimately in damage to the tire. Distorted rim elements can cause premature failure of the tire at the bead.

Because of such corrosion troubles, it has become recommended practice for truck-tire rims to be wire-brushed and otherwise freed of accumulated rust and repainted each time a tire change is made. Rim manufacturers say that if this is done religiously, the rims should outlast the rest of a truck. Distorted flanges should, of course, be repaired or replaced.

34882

CONTROLLED BEADS AND BEAD-LOCKING DEVICES

A CHIEF REASON why a deflated tire is ruined quickly if the vehicle continues to be driven is that the beads become unseated from the rim and permit the casing to be excessively distorted, torn, etc. For military use, there was developed a system of locking beads on the rim, plus a "combat" type of tire which could be operated under "run-flat" conditions. When its beads are anchored to the rim, it is possible to drive such a tire, when deflated, for many miles before it disintegrates—under some conditions, it is reported, as many as 100 miles. This is the general background for two developments involving beads and rims.

One of these developments, introduced and used during World War II, is a bead lock for tactical combat vehicles, and is reminiscent of locking devices or spreaders used in tires 40 years or so previously. A metal band is installed so that it encircles the central portion of the rim base and lies between the tire beads. When the side ring of a divided rim is placed, the beads are gripped between the edges of the central band and the rim flanges. If the air is shot from a tire, the beads still are held in place, and the vehicle can continue to roll.

Spring-clip Bead Lock. The bead-locking band was a relatively heavy device, and subsequently was replaced by a spring-clip bead hook. This is a simple, inexpensive clip stamped from sheet steel and installed between the tire bead and rim. It is shaped so that, when slipped over the bead, it grips it with slight compression. This enables the tire to be handled without losing clips. The other end of the clip extends around and grips the rim flange. From 10 to 14 of these clips are installed in each tire. When the tire is deflated, they lock the beads in position on the rim, so the tire can be driven without air for several miles. The clips prevent the driving wheels from slipping around inside the casings.

ADVICE TO INVENTORS

*I*N THE LONG history of tires, various developments have become known by the names of their inventors. There is the Welch tire, the Bartlett clincher, and so on. But Thomas Midgley, a prolific inventor credited with developing such improvements as a piano-wire bead and multiple

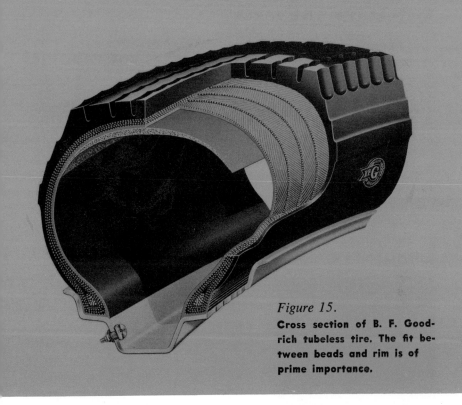

beads, is said to have advised inventors not to let their names become tags for their brain children. According to the story, he based his advice on a bit of sad experience.

One of his inventions had become commonly known as the Midgley quick-detachable rim. One day, while driving along a road, he stopped behind a stalled automobile, whose driver, now standing beside it, was making the air sizzle with his opinions of motoring and of rims in particular. Gradually it became apparent to Midgley that the quick-detachable part of one of the stalled car's rims had decided to detach itself while the machine was approaching the brow of a hill. The driver had succeeded in stopping without upsetting; but the rim flange, along with the tire which had taken off after it, now was reposing far ahead, at the bottom of the hill. In keeping with motoring etiquette, Midgley asked whether he could be of any help. Instead of replying directly, the stalled motorist declared that "if I could get my hands on that _____ Midgley who invented this rim, I'd wrap what's left of it around his neck!"

Thereupon Midgley, probably vowing never again to let his name become known in association with a product he had invented, diplomatically backed away and continued his trip.

RIM PROGRESS

$\mathcal{T}$ECHNICIANS WHO are concerned with the development of pneumatic-tire equipment do not consider present-day rims to be perfect—and they do not agree with one another as to what future developments are likely to be. The tubeless tire has made the fit between bead and rim of prime importance, and, in this connection, rubber compounds and adhesion have played a big part. Further refinement of tubeless-tire rims may be expected.

In the opinion of some, the drop-center rim leaves a great deal to be

AUTOMOBILE RIM TYPES

Clincher Rim	One-piece rim for soft-bead clincher tires used exclusively during 1900–1905. Was a development of single-clinch bicycle rim. Bicycle-type tires other than clincher were, for a time, unavailable for automobiles, partly because of the lack of suitable rims. At first, stay bolts or spreaders, spaced around rim to hold beads against flanges, were considered necessary.
Quick-detachable or Q.D. Rim	Introduced in 1905. Q.D. clincher rim used with clincher tires having inextensible beads made usually of fabric and hard rubber. Q.D. straight-side rim used with tires whose sides were straight and without clinches, and which had inextensible beads reinforced with wire. The Q.D. rim had a removable side ring or flange to permit tire to be slid on or off rim base.
Split Rim	Rim split or having removable section so it could be bent inward to reduce its diameter and thus permit tire to be removed. Used primarily with straight-side tire. A variation: split rim hinged at point opposite split.

desired. Installing and removing a tire often inflicts punishment on the beads and other parts of the casing, sometimes as a result of the carelessness or ignorance of the person doing the work. The ancient idea of stretching clincher beads in order to get them on or off a rim apparently has held over to present times, for it is possible to find people who still think that the wire-reinforced beads of modern straight-sidewall tires can be stretched—and sometimes an uninformed tire changer will try to do just that. One disadvantage of the drop-center rim is that on a wheel of limited diameter, it restricts the size of the brake drum that can be installed. Because of increasing demands being made on the braking facilities of motor cars, some manufacturers are said to be considering a return to the quick-detachable type of rim. By eliminating the hollow rim

Universal Q.D. Rim	Rim base equipped with two reversible flanges and a locking ring for outer, or front, flange. Would accommodate either clincher or straight-side tire according to position of flanges.
Demountable Rim	Clincher, quick-detachable, or universal rim mounted so it could be removed easily from wheel felloe. Locked in place by lugs, bolts, and nuts.
Hollow-center, Depressed-center, or Drop-center Rim	First used around 1890. Reintroduced into the United States from Europe in the 1920's and later generally adopted. Resembles original one-piece clincher rim to the extent that it has no "moving parts."
Demountable Wheels	Introduction of wire-spoke and disk wheels led to practice of making rim and wheel a unit demountable at the hub. Not always wholly practical when tire sizes are so great that extra weight of wheel disk or spokes is objectionable, as in large truck sizes.

center, a brake drum of greater diameter could be installed without going to larger-diameter tires.

A veteran rim designer recalls that, back in earlier days when quick-detachable demountable rims were in use, a company shipped a set of tires to a taxi operator in an Eastern city. The operator installed the tires on a cab, and it was driven for several months before someone discovered that the detachable flanges had been omitted. The tires had been run without anything to hold the beads in place other than their strength and tightness on the rim base. This has suggested to the rim designer that perhaps the flanges could be modified greatly or even omitted, since they serve primarily as props anyway. Of course, many older motorists who used quick-detachable rims may remember incidents when the tires did not stick so tightly. The writer remembers a hair-raising experience when, as a boy, he was riding down a hill in a Chalmers touring car which suddenly shed both flange and tire—much in the manner of the car in the Midgley episode. But the tight-fitting beads possible today, like those on the taxicab, might minimize the flange.

In trucking circles there is a tendency to return to the demountable rim because it makes possible a lighter tire assembly than when the entire wheel is demountable at the hub. When truck operators pay for their tires on a mileage basis, and tires and rims must be handled a lot in the course of inspections and servicing, weight of tire assemblies and convenience in handling them become important.

Whatever the direction of future development, the tire and its rim will proceed hand in hand, for they are as closely related as a lock and its key. Bead refinements will be reflected in rim changes, and vice versa—for the tire bead and the rim on which it rests must work together in forming a connecting link between tire and wheel.

Today, in contrast with conditions existing in the earlier days of the automobile, a tire made by any reliable manufacturer will fit a corresponding rim of any make. This situation is the result of work done by The Tire and Rim Association, Incorporated, the governing body on tires and rims, which bases its operations at Akron, Ohio. The Association establishes standards governing rim and tire dimensions and tolerances, the positions of valve holes, and similar details. By adhering to these standards, tire and rim manufacturers make it possible for a motorist—no matter where he may be—to buy and install a new tire with full confidence that it will fit his rim properly. The Association maintains inspectors in tire and rim factories, who keep constant check on the products to make certain that they meet requirements.

CHAPTER 4 § BEAD TYPES

T HE USE of beads in pneumatic tires was antedated by the use of beadlike edges and wire reinforcements in solid-rubber and cushion tires for carriages, bicycles, and other vehicles. Although these details usually could be called beads only by the most active imagination, they undoubtedly had some influence on later thinking with respect to pneumatic-tire beads.

WIRE IN NONPNEUMATIC TIRES

A T FIRST, the wire placed in a solid or cushion tire to keep it from stretching too much consisted of a single strand running approximately through the center of the tire. This arrangement had a fault: the rubber

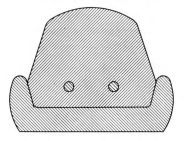

Figure 1.

Antedating wire in beads were the wires used in solid-rubber tires to hold them more securely on wheels. Wire ends were butt-welded.

55

tended to rotate around the wire, and thus the tire would twist and come off the rim. Then it was discovered that if two wire rings were embedded in a solid tire, each a short distance in from the rim flange and rim base, the tire no longer had a tendency to rotate around the reinforcement, and thus would stay in place better.

Other ways of using wires in conjunction with nonpneumatic rubber tires have been mentioned in preceding chapters.

EARLY TIRE-WIRE PATENTS

$\mathcal{B}$EFORE REASONABLE order was established in the design of clincher and straight-side tires, resulting in the adoption of a relatively small number of bead constructions, there was a great deal of inventive activity involving wire-reinforced beads and nonbead wire in tires. Few of these ideas seemed to get beyond the patent stage, but most of them influenced subsequent thinking.

A pneumatic bead with a thick base and an "endless binding wire" positioned well toward the sidewall was designed by W. Turner. This was used on a rim resembling those later adopted for the straight-side tire. When it was desired to remove the tire, one of the beads was turned on its side, the enlarged edge or base being forced toward the rim center, which was flat. This moved the wire reinforcement closer to the rim, so that the diametrically opposite portion of the bead could be pulled over the rim flange. Then the same was done with the remaining bead (Figure 2).

A two-piece tire depending on wires embedded in the tread to hold it together was invented by G. C. Douglas in Great Britain. Each tire half consisted of a sidewall, tread section, and an inextensible bead that hooked over the outward-curved rim flange. Saw-toothed grooves were formed in the tread sections, on the outside of one and the inside of the other, so the two tread halves would lock together; and to prevent them from unlocking, several wires forming circumferential rings were embedded in the outer tread rubber (Figure 3).

Hinged Beads. A tire having metal bead rings hinged so the beads could be snapped over the rounded edges of a flat rim was devised by S. A. Stanfield, a British inventor. The rings were tightened by inflating the tire.

56

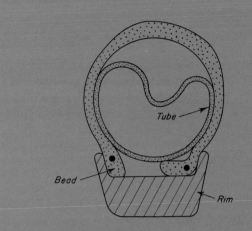

Figure 2.

In this tire, bead reinforcement was placed so portion of bead between it and the flat-base rim could be turned on its side thus permitting opposite side to be pulled over flange (W. Turner, British patent 721 of 1893).

Figure 3.

Two-piece tire having wire-reinforced tread sections which hooked together (G. C. Douglas, British patent 1613 of 1893).

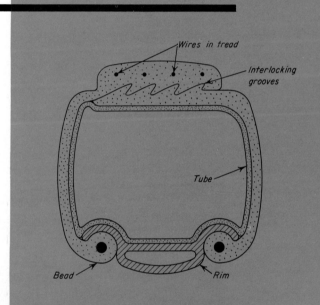

Figure 4.

The inventor called this tire construction "watertight" (W. R. Foster, British patent 6676 of 1893).

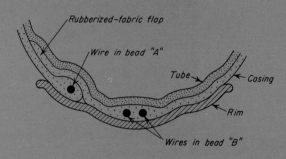

"B" is installed first
"A" is sprung into rim to position indicated

A "watertight" tire, invented in England by W. R. Foster, had one wire-reinforced bead positioned in the center of the rim when the tire was in place, and a rubberized-fabric flap extending around between the tube and sidewall. This flap formed a cover for the second beaded edge, which rested in a rim groove in much the same way as the bead of a Dunlop tire of that period (Figure 4).

Interlocking Edges. A variation of the previous invention was suggested by F. G. Preston and consisted of interlocking beaded edges positioned near one flange of the rim. One bead was reinforced with a cord; the other, of somewhat smaller circumference, with a wire. After the tire was in place, the ends of the wire were pulled through holes in the rim and tied (Figure 5).

A tire having three beads reinforced by wire was patented by W. H. Cresswell in England. Two bead wires were conventionally placed in the tire, but extending beyond one bead was a canvas-rubber flap having a third bead along its outer edge. This flap bridged the space above the rim center, and its bead was shaped and positioned so that it formed an interlocking joint with the first bead. Inflation pressure held everything in place (Figure 6).

Figure 5.

Interlocking beaded edges, one reinforced with wire, the other with cord (F. G. Preston, British patent 21,078 of 1893).

Figure 6.

Early tire design incorporating three beads reinforced with wire (W. H. Cresswell, British patent 22,894 of 1893).

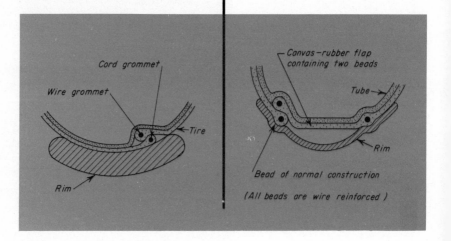

Helical-spring reinforcements were used in beads of a tire patented in Great Britain by D. H. Smith. The steel springs could be flattened, if desired, to conform to bead shape. The projecting spring-reinforced edges were to be bound on the rim with metal bands or something similar. Later, P. E. Doolittle of Toronto, Canada, also suggested the use of coil-spring reinforcements (Figure 7).

Bead Plus Removable Flange. The removable ring of later-day quick-detachable rims was foreshadowed in a bead arrangement patented by W. P. Thompson. The rim base had a full-sized integral flange on one side, and the wire-reinforced edge of the tire casing was placed on a cylindrical seat. The inventor suggested that the casing could be riveted in place if desired. The bead seat on the other side of the rim was formed by a removable flange ring, on which the inextensible second bead rested (Figure 8).

Elastic rings or hoops, made of round steel wire or flat bands of spring steel, were used as bead reinforcements by Leopold Holt, of Frankfort, Germany, in a tire he designed. He made the hoops with overlapping ends and shaped them so that when free, they were of smaller circumference than the flat-base rim. The tire was installed on the rim by

Figure 7.
Beads reinforced with wire in helical-spring form (D. H. Smith, British patent 11,527 of 1893).

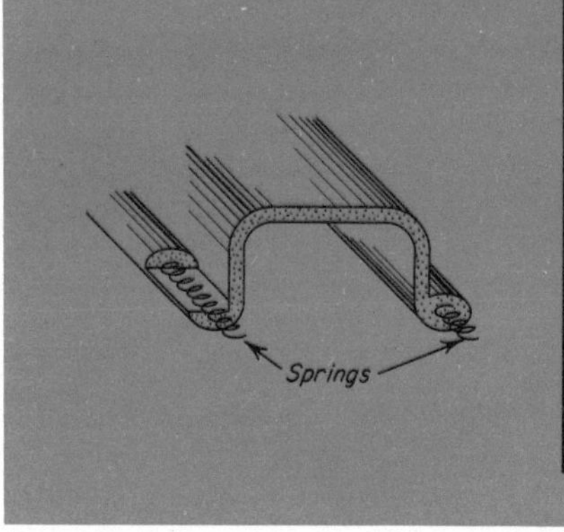

Figure 8.
This bead arrangement foreshadowed later-day quick detachable rims (W. P. Thompson, British patent 22,554 of 1893).

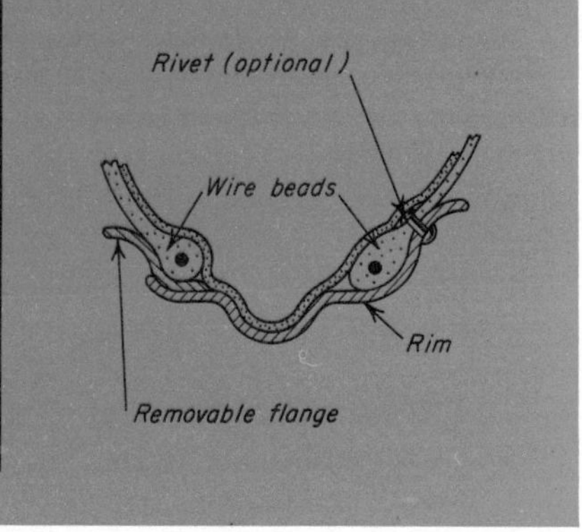

expanding these bead reinforcements; and after the beads were properly seated, the ends of the hoops were clamped by a locking bolt and plate, setscrews, or other arrangement.

Chain-reinforced Beads. Among the numerous kinds of reinforcements suggested for tire beads, it is to be expected that chains would be found. Such a construction was used by Joseph G. Moomy, of Erie, Pennsylvania. He preferred the flat-link "dog chain," which, being stamped from sheet metal, has little stretch and links not likely to separate.

Cut-away Flange. Robert P. Scott, of Cadiz, Ohio, brother of "Nip" Scott of braided-wire fame, patented, in 1894, a scheme for making easier the installing and removing of bicycle tires having inextensible wire beads. Instead of the Dunlop-type hollow-center rim, he used a flat-base rim and cut away a portion of its flange. The cut extended for a distance of about two spaces between wheel spokes. After placing the tire around the rest of the rim, he would force the beads over the cutout portion of the flange and on the rim base, then install the removable flange section and lock it in place with a metal pin (Figure 9).

Two Beads Plus. A tire somewhat like Cresswell's three-bead arrangement (page 58) was worked out by H. J. Doughty, of Providence, Rhode Island, in 1898. His tire casing, mounted on a crescent-shaped rim, was provided with two inextensible beads containing wire or other reinforcement and lying wholly outside the rim. Extending across the rim face from each bead was a canvas flap, the two overlapping to form a joint, between rim and inner tube, that was supposed not to admit moisture and dirt. The flaps could be plain and depend on friction to hold them in place, but Doughty suggested that one be provided with a beaded edge fitting in a groove in the other flap, thus making the two flaps interlocking (Figure 10).

One-bead Tire. In another patent, Doughty described a tire having only one wire-reinforced bead. This, too, was positioned outside the crescent-shaped rim. The casing was made of a continuous, flexible strip, shaped in cross section so that it would wrap twice around the inner tube, forming a two-thickness covering. Friction and the inextensible bead were said to hold the tire securely in place once the tube had been inflated (Figure 11).

Scott Wire-fabric Reinforcement. Charles S. Scott, of Cadiz, Ohio, better known in tire circles as "Nip" Scott, was granted a patent in 1898 (No. 608,273) covering the use of "shrinkable metal fabric;" such as "diagonally-woven" (braided) wire fabric, as reinforcement in single-

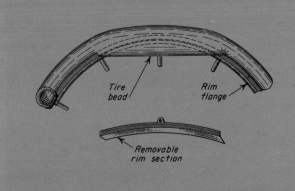

Figure 9.

In a method of mounting bicycle tires devised by Robert P. Scott, a section of rim flange was removed to permit the non-extensible beads to be mounted on the rim. The section, when replaced, was held in position by a pin (patent 521,273, 1894).

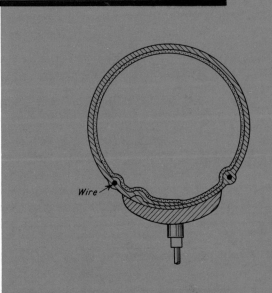

Figure 10.

This tire had its beads outside the rim! Canvas flaps extending from each beaded edge overlapped to form a joint said to have been resistant to water and dirt (H. J. Doughty patent 608,188, 1898).

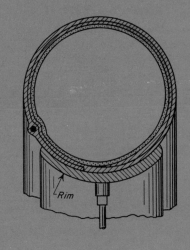

Figure 11.

This tire, developed in 1898, had only one wire-reinforced bead, and it was located outside the rim area. The casing wrapped twice around the inner tube (H. J. Doughty patent 608,187, 1898).

tube and two-part tires fitting crescent-shaped rims. He installed the wire fabric as two endless strips or bands of tape secured to or embedded in the fabric-rubber shoe (casing). Each strip was placed so that one edge would be below the rim flange, the other edge above it. When the tire was inflated, the strips were distorted; and Scott claimed that this action tended to prevent the tire from creeping in either direction. He explained that when a pair of endless wires is installed in the tire below the wheel-rim edges, there is a tendency of the tire to creep in one direction; when the wires are installed above the level of the edges, the tendency is to creep in the opposite direction. So, by extending the wire-fabric strips both above and below the rim edges, the two creeping tendencies are made to neutralize each other. Later, in 1905, Scott was issued another patent (No. 770,611) covering the use of a "woven-wire tape" as a bead reinforcement in pneumatic tires; and this was an important factor in the success of the straight-side tire, as already mentioned. The inventor, in referring to "woven-wire" tape, evidently had in mind a construction now commonly known as wire braid (Figure 12).

"Angle-iron" Beads. A pair of inventors, Edward E. Preston and Charles E. Sibson, of Leicester, England, employed, in a tire they designed, beads reinforced with ring-shaped bands having a cross section somewhat like that of a piece of angle iron. When the tire was inflated, these "angular-shaped or concave-faced" bands rested on "angular-shaped beadings" or seats in the steel rim. When the tube was deflated, one beaded edge of the tire could be pushed off its seat and into the hollow center of the rim, permitting the tire to be removed (Figure 13).

Figure 12.
Charles S. Scott called the reinforcement embedded in his bicycle tire of 1898 "diagonally woven wire fabric." It is considered an early form of flat-wire braid (patent 608,273, 1898).

Figure 13.
Truly inextensible beads were suggested by Preston and Sibson. Steel rings, resembling angle iron in cross section, were embedded in beaded edges (patent 620,252, 1899).

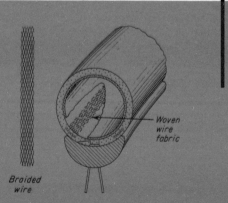

Woven wire fabric

Braided wire

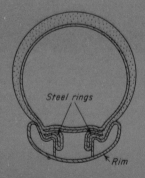

Steel rings

Rim

Irwin Patents. Over a period ranging from 1901 to 1905, H. E. Irwin, of Galesburg, Illinois, patented a number of methods of mounting pneumatic tires on rims and keeping them there. Starting with a clincher tire and rim combination, he devised an inner tube having, around its inner circumference, a rib made of fabric and shaped to fit in the V-notch or groove between the toes of the beads. When the tube was inflated, this rib prevented it from being pinched between the beads and, at the same time, acted as a wedge to force the beads into the rim-flange channels. To prevent the tire from slipping around the rim in heavy pulling, Irwin proposed that the casing be notched in the bead regions at intervals so that the beaded edges could straddle bolts, screws, pins, or staples installed transversely in the rim channel. Another idea he had was to employ bolts installed radially in the rim and acting like miniature jackscrews to force a metal band against the beaded edges, which, in his tire design, came together in the center of the rim channel: the pressure of the band served to lock the beads in the rim-flange channels.

Irwin also patented a method of locking a tire on its clincher rim by means of pins or staples formed of steel wire and inserted through holes in the rim flanges and beads. To facilitate the installing or removing of clincher tires on one-piece rims, he proposed that several rents or cuts be made to sever the beads, and that above each rent, wire or fabric tape be embedded in the rubber to act as a strengthening bridge. The staple-shaped pins, which were said to lock the beads to the rim even when the tire was deflated, were installed to straddle the rents. (A need for locking beads to rims arose later in connection with tires for military vehicles.)

In a 1904 patent, Irwin covered a method of fastening solid, cushion, and single-tube pneumatic tires to rims by means of "woven-wire" (braided) tape or fabric embedded in the tire structure. He proposed various fastening devices for anchoring the wire fabric to the wheel rim, or felly. One of his suggestions was that a tire be constructed to fit over and around the edges of a conventional flat carriage-wheel tire (steel hoop), where it is held by bolts, screws, or other fasteners; and he recommended that the rubber tire be removed so the wheels could be run on the steel tires in winter, ". . . as rubber tires are not of so much value then" (Figure 14).

Turnbuckle Fastenings. Various ways were devised for clamping tires on rims with rings or bands whose ends were joined by turnbuckles. In the arrangement illustrated in Figure 15, side wires whose ends are united by turnbuckles clamp the tire bases or beads, which are reinforced by internal wires or bands, to the rim. This method was patented by John Neary, of Kokomo, Indiana.

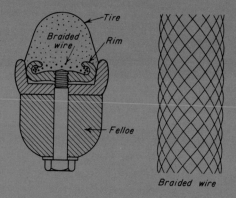

Figure 14

Method of mounting tire suggested by H. E. Irwin (Patent 753,401).

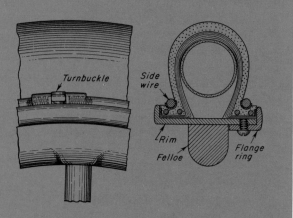

Figure 15

This tire was provided with wire-reinforced beads, which were clamped to the rim by side wires equipped with turnbuckles for tightening (John Neary patent 779,731, 1905).

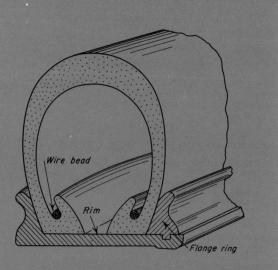

Figure 16.

Here the bead-grommets have been placed inside the casing but not inside the beaded edges. They rested in grooves formed by inward-turning beads. (Arthur von Lüde patent 780,209, 1905).

Wires in Channels. One inventor, Arthur von Lüde, arranged his bead wires so that instead of being embedded in the structure of the tire, they rested in channels formed in the thickened edges of the casing. The tire was mounted on a rim having a detachable flange, and the channels were on the inside of the casing (Figure 16).

WIRE IN OTHER PARTS OF TIRE

*N*UMEROUS SUGGESTIONS have been made for incorporating wire in pneumatic-tire treads in order to discourage punctures and to gain other supposed advantages. In Great Britain, J. A. Harrison worked out a scheme for placing wires, running side by side circumferentially, to form armored layers either near the outer surface of the tread or between the tread and fabric plies. A. S. Allen, of Brookline, Massachusetts, describes, in a U.S. patent issued to him in 1906, tire armor composed largely of intermeshed wire coils, some of which were carried into the bead portions of the casing. In the beads, he had a "series of intermeshed edge coils" and cord reinforcements. Allen also described a textile covering for his wires, which he said would produce better bonding with the rubber.

Midgley Wire-cord Tire. A tire having more wire in its make-up than usual was developed by Thomas Midgley, of Hartford, Connecticut, and patented in 1909. He employed strands of wire cable positioned obliquely much like the cords in a cord tire. The cables of one ply were at right angles to those of adjacent plies; and he devised helical, spring-like stays to interlace with these tension cables. The diagonal cables were passed around beads composed of strands of wire, or were looped over hooks attached to the bead wires.

"Woven-wire" fabric was specified as armor for a tire devised by John Anthony, of Attleboro, Massachusetts. He made the bead reinforcements from strips of similar material bent into tubular form. Such reinforcements were said to be sufficiently yielding to be used in clincher beads.

The inventors who proposed tire casings armored throughout with wire were not idle dreamers, for today wire-cord tires are in use on trucks and other heavy-duty vehicles.

The foregoing inventions are indicative of some of the ways in which a reliable union between a tire and its rim has been sought. Of course, as in any field of technical trial and error, relatively few of the ideas put forward ever attained commercial success. A considerable number, though not in themselves of any practical importance, exerted an influence on later bead developments. Out of the maelstrom of imagination, whose scope is merely suggested by the patents mentioned, there came a comparatively small number of bead designs which proved to be practical, and which have given us the reliable tires of today.

THREE PRACTICAL BEAD TYPES

*I*N THE entire history of pneumatic automobile tires, there have been but three practical types; and the differences between them have been almost wholly in their bead construction. The situation is summarized in the following table.

Tire	Bead	Rim
Regular clincher	Soft: extensible	One-piece
Quick-detachable clincher	Hard rubber and fabric, hard rubber and string, or wire-reinforced: inextensible	Split or removable side ring
Straight-sidewall or "straight-side"	Wire-reinforced: inextensible	Split, removable side ring, or drop-center

The enlarged edges of tire casings, called beads, can be divided into two types:

1. Those containing bands, wires, rods, and other shapes made usually of steel.

2. Those containing no metal reinforcement.

The soft-bead or "regular" clincher tire mounted on a one-piece rim had to have beads that were elastic enough to be stretched over the rim flanges. A typical bead of this kind consisted of a rubber core covered with a layer of square-woven cotton drill, friction-coated with rubber. The core at first was molded straight and partly cured; then its ends were spliced to form a ring. In later construction, the core, formed by extruding the rubber compound on a tubing machine, was spliced to form a ring, placed in a mold, and partly cured. Then the frictioned cover was applied. In either case, the fabric-covered core next was placed on the tire casing, and fabric plies were folded over it.

The core of the regular clincher bead usually was made of a compound that became quite hard when cured and was called either "semisoft" or "semihard." In spite of its hardness, the bead rubber had to withstand considerable elongation without being damaged.

One tire manufacturer's records indicate that the rubber compound used as core material in clincher beads had a sulfur content of 15 per cent, and when cured had a Shore Durometer A hardness of 88 to 92. This rubber compound was not always used alone. In one clincher construction, textile fibers were mixed with it to increase stiffness. In another construction, bias-cut frictioned fabric was rolled into a "snake" (tube) and incorporated into the bead core as a reinforcement which was stretchable.

The quick-detachable clincher tire, which was the predecessor of the wire-bead, straight-side type, did not have to stretch over the rim flange, so its bead core could be inextensible. Actually, the core often was not wholly inextensible. Several constructions were used, including:

1. A rubber core of considerable hardness and having negligible elongation. The compound was a high-sulfur type. If this bead cracked, the fabric at the break would split.

2. Ground friction fabric mixed with rubber compound and semicured. This produced a core having a high fiber content. It was wrapped with square-woven frictioned fabric cut on a bias.

3. Cord, thread, string, or fabric strips twisted to form cords, wound together to give the proper cross section, covered with frictioned bias fabric, and semicured to shape.

4. A single heavy wire, ends brazed to make an endless ring, covered with semihard rubber or ground friction fabric; the covering was semicured in a mold before installation in a tire.

5. A single strand of tinned high-carbon piano wire, of a diameter such as 0.054 inch, wound a number of times around a form, and ends soldered. The resulting ring, hoop, or bead-grommet then was sandwiched between strips of semihard rubber compound and semicured in a mold. Or the wire core was wrapped with frictioned fabric in strip form. This construction was called the piano-wire bead. Larger-diameter wires used at first were supplanted later by ones of smaller diameter.

67

The straight-side detachable tire got its foothold in 1905 when Goodyear introduced a "no-rim-cut" tire having beads containing wire braid, and Firestone brought out a straight-side having wire-cable beads. The straight-side and the quick-detachable (Q.D.) clincher tire periods overlapped, just as the regular clincher and quick-detachable clincher periods had done. During this overlapping period, when most quick-detachable clincher tires had semi-inextensible beads, the quick-detachable clincher made by Goodyear actually was a straight-side tire having wire reinforcement in the beads and dummy clincher beads, held in place by chafing strips of rubberized fabric. This tire, although it looked like a clincher and fitted a clincher rim, actually behaved as a straight-side, the bead wire doing most of the work of holding it on the rim.

Records indicate that braided bead wire was used by Goodyear in straight-side tires exclusively from about 1905 to 1916—with the exception that some American Michelin tires were made with braid manufactured and sold to Michelin by Goodyear; and that, beginning around 1911, braided wire made by wire companies appeared on the market in limited quantities, and other tire manufacturers began using it. Braid became the standard reinforcement for beads of high-pressure tires. Around 1920, various tire manufacturers developed means of employing cables, woven tapes, and single wires. These will be treated more fully in later chapters.

NONWIRE BEAD REINFORCEMENTS

*A*MONG THE various nonwire beads that have been used or tested are the following:

Fiber Beads. As already mentioned, threads or cords of cotton were saturated with rubber in solution and wound or otherwise combined into a ring, which then was wrapped with friction-coated fabric. But in the course of attempts to improve beads, other materials have been considered. These included fibers of manila hemp, hemp, flax, jute, pineapple, silk, and glass, plus many more of similar type. Such fibrous materials were made into rope form for testing; and they all proved to have two common, negative characteristics: excessive elongation and poor adhesion to rubber.

To overcome the elongation, attempts were made to destretch the materials, but this did not prove successful. There was some research work done on adhesion between various fibers and rubber; but because

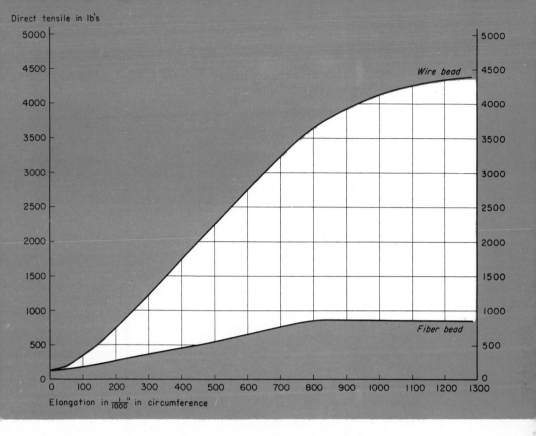

Figure 17. **Elongation tests on steel wire and fiber beads.**

of the negative results already achieved with respect to elongation, etc., this phase of the work soon was dropped.

Tires containing beads reinforced with glass fibers, which have high tensile strength, were run on test cars over an extended period by the National-Standard Company. They did not prove commercially practical.

Another drawback encountered in the studies of fibrous materials for beads was the difficulty of handling them in production. This was because the bead-grommets were very flimsy.

During the history of the tire, inventors have given some thought to bead-grommets made of fibrous materials. In a patent covering fibrous beads, Stephen A. Reed, of Duxbury, Massachusetts, suggests a "particular organization" of hard vegetable fibers such as manila hemp, hemp, and sisal. Flexibility and resistance to corrosion are mentioned.

Courson's Band. This was a flat, perforated band of steel, installed in much the same manner as wire braid or tape.

69

PATENTS MENTIONED IN CHAPTER 4

Inventor	U.S.	British	Year
Allen, A. S.	835,005		1906
Anthony, John	1,003,314		1911
Cresswell, W. H.		22,894	1893
Doolittle, P. E.	788,710		1905
Doughty, H. J.	608,187		1898
	608,188		1898
Douglas, G. C.		1,613	1893
Foster, W. R.		6,676	1893
Harrison, J. A.		22,080	1893
Holt, Leopold	509,903		1893
Irwin, H. E.	680,486		
	735,265		
	745,443		1901–05
	753,401		
	798,185		
Midgley, Thomas	913,220		1909
Moomy, Joseph G.	501,290		1893
Neary, John	779,731		1905
Preston, F. G.		21,078	1893
Preston, E. E., and Sibson, C. E.	620,252		1899
Reed, Stephen A.	2,081,096		1937
Scott, Charles S.	608,273		1898
	770,611		1905
Scott, Robert P.	521,273		1894
Smith, D. H.		11,527	1893
Stanfield, S. A.		5,187	1893
Thompson, W. P.		22,554	1893
Turner, W.		721	1893
Von Lüde, Arthur	780,209		1905

CHAPTER 5 § WIRE IN BEADS

OF THE VARIOUS materials tried as reinforcements in the beads of straight-side pneumatic tires, ranging from the Dunlop-Welch bicycle tire to the present-day automobile casing, steel wire, in one form or another, has been found the only material that will support the bead for the expected life of the tire.

Wire reinforcements in automobile-tire beads began their climb to popularity early in the present century. During the period of 1900 to 1905, the regular, or soft-bead, clincher tire, having no wire in it, was brought to a state of high development. It began to look like the only type that ever would be standard. But with the introduction of rims having removable flanges, beads no longer had to stretch an inch or more; and the quick-detachable bead having textile fibers, cords, wire, or other inelastic materials embedded in its rubber came into use. Moreover, around 1905, came the straight-side idea—which really was a revival of the original Dunlop scheme—and tire beads had to have great strength in addition to being inextensible. The simplest and most effective way of making a bead strong and practically stretchless is to embed a wire bead-grommet in it.

At first, the wire-reinforced bead of the straight-side tire naturally met a lot of opposition from clincher-bead manufacturers. At one stage in the situation, the makers of clincher tires introduced a quick-detachable type having a wire-reinforced bead equipped with a clincher hook. In such a tire, the hook was largely a kind of luxury, for it was not required to hold on the rim a tire already reinforced with a wire bead to perform the same function. More material was needed for this bead than for a straight-side type, the clincher tire held less air, and the tire was more difficult to install on a rim because of the heavier beads. Eventually the quick-detachable clincher with its inextensible bead disappeared, leaving the clincher-tire field to the regular type, which remained in use but fought a losing battle for almost 40 years; while the straight-side, with its wire-reinforced beads, grew in popularity until it became the only type in general use.

Some of the most important wire reinforcements for beads will be described in this chapter.

FLAT WIRE BRAID (INTRODUCED 1905)

*A*LTHOUGH WIRE had been used as a reinforcement in pneumatic cycle-tire beads as far back as 1890, it was not until 1905 that it became established as an essential part of pneumatic automobile tires. The use of flat wire braid in automobile-tire beads began in that year, when Charles S. Scott, of Cadiz, Ohio, contracted with the Goodyear Tire & Rubber Company to supply braid for the new Goodyear straight-side tires. Later, the demand for Scott's braid became greater than his plant capacity, so part of the braiding operations were moved from Cadiz to the Goodyear plant at Akron, where, as valuable industrial secrets, they were carried on for many years behind locked doors. Eventually others acquired the necessary braiding equipment and know-how, and braided beads came into general use.

Flat wire braid is produced on machines that braid an odd number of strands together, usually in an "over two, under two" or "plain-braid" pattern. Wire made from various metals can be used, but for tire beads steel wire is employed. This wire usually has either a liquor-drawn or an AP-1 (copper over zinc) finish. Although the more widely used braids are the 9-, 13-, 17-, and 21-wire sizes, braid may be made of from 3 to 29 or more wires—but the number of wires is always uneven. The wire sizes most commonly used for tire beads are 0.025 and 0.028 inch. However, there is almost limitless flexibility in the tensile characteristics of braid; that is, the sizes, strength, and number of wires can be varied widely; and the bead-grommet strength can be further controlled by varying the number of convolutions, or turns, of braid.

The following table will give some idea of common braid sizes.

Braid Advantages. Flat wire braid has been used so extensively in tires because it possesses important advantages over other steel reinforcements, during both the manufacturing and the operational stages. The flexibility of braid makes it able to withstand abuse that would badly damage or ruin another type of bead reinforcement. Where a cable, for

BRAID
.028″ DIAMETER WIRE
Average tensile per strand — 140 lbs. (230,000 psi)

Strand	Wire Diameter	Total Tensile	Approx. Width	Wt. per 1000 ft.
9	.028	1260	.219	18.59
13	.028	1820	.320	27.60
17	.028	2380	.370	37.00
21	.028	2940	.440	45.60

BRAID
.025″ DIAMETER WIRE
Average tensile per strand — 113 lbs. (230,000 psi)

Strand	Wire Diameter	Total Tensile	Approx. Width	Wt. per 1000 ft.
9	.025	1017	.203	16.25
13	.025	1469	.250	23.25
17	.025	1921	.352	30.25
21	.025	2373	.420	37.00

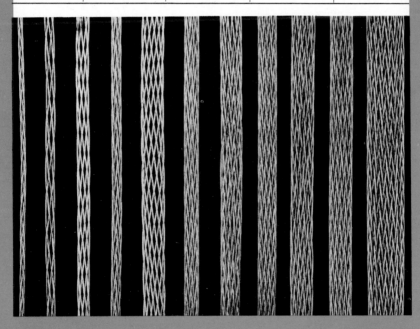

Figure 1. **Flat wire braid, from 5 to 29 strand.**

instance, would absorb the entire force of a shock because of its stiffness and lack of elasticity, braid subjected to the same shock would yield enough to prevent it from being damaged.

The wire finish and its effects on adhesion between braid and adjacent rubber can be the same as for other forms of wire bead reinforcement. However, braid possesses an additional advantage: its shape permits it to achieve a better mechanical unity with rubber. Although the individual wires forming the braid are close together, the way in which they are interwoven produces innumerable openings between wires. Rubber applied to the braid in any of various ways will, during the curing period, fill all these openings; and when the rubber compound hardens and toughens as a result of vulcanization, it anchors the wires firmly. This anchoring action, often called "riveting" because of the countless rubber "rivets" involved, is what enabled braid to supplant single wire, which was tried as a tire reinforcement in the beginning days.

Braid has been made by braiding stranded wire, such as the 19-wire beading strand (see page 77), but generally it is manufactured from single wires of high-carbon steel, cold-worked to develop the required physical characteristics.

A considerable number of methods have been employed in the converting of flat wire braid into a ring-shaped bead reinforcement, or bead-grommet. In earlier days, the braid was made into a bead-grommet without first being rubber-coated. Some manufacturers would wrap the bare braid around a bead former, making as many turns as required to produce the desired strength. Then they would wrap the resulting ring with skim-coated fabric, place the bead in a mold, and precure it. This operation would force the skim coat of rubber into the interstices of the braid. A variation was to wind a strip of uncured rubber compound along with the braid, so that the finished bead-grommet had rubber sandwiched between the convolutions of wire. The bead-grommet then was wrapped with fabric and cured. A third method, and the one that finally became standard, is to run the braid through an insulating head that coats and fills it with rubber compound, after which it is wound on a bead former to produce a ring-shaped bead-grommet. Most companies fasten one or both ends of the braid with friction tape or wire staples.

The practice of curing beads *before* they were put into a tire was discontinued as soon as advances in rubber technology permitted. As nearly as can be estimated, the precure method was discontinued by one company in 1916, and after that date other companies gradually adopted the practice of using uncured beads. At first, the beads were cold-pressed into form; later on, the cold pressing was discontinued, and the beads were simply made into rings and put directly into the tire.

In the early days when the storage of tires was a problem, uncured tires were hung on pins or laid on the floor, and their beads became kinked. Braid, with its flexibility, seemed to lend itself better to such handling, in that the kinks were less severe and were relieved in the curing of the tire. This advantage of braid was forcibly brought out when a more rigid bead was later developed, and the kinking problem became acute.

Some ways of arranging wire in tire beads are described below.

0.054-INCH TINNED (PIANO) WIRE (1906–1940)

FOR A CONSIDERABLE period (about 1906 to 1939 or 1940) a widely used type of bead reinforcement was that known as the "054 ferruled." This consisted of 0.054-inch tinned high-carbon, high-tensile wire wound into a ring of the required number of convolutions. The ends were joined by means of solder, one or two ferrules, and sometimes twisting. Various ways of making the joint included:

1. Ends butted and covered with a ferrule whose edges were separated enough to admit solder.

2. Ends overlapped a short distance, covered with a slotted ferrule, and soldered.

3. Ends overlapped 7 inches or so until previously made scratch marks were in alignment (to give proper ring size), then twisted together one complete turn; two tapered ferrules tightened over ends of wires, and the joint then dipped into solder.

4. "Mansfield" splice (1920's to about 1935); wire ends twisted together three or four times; fine bright-finish wire (about 0.015-inch diameter) wound for $\frac{3}{4}$ inch along each end of splice to bind wire ends, like ferrules. Joint soft-soldered.

Making Bead-grommet. A typical method of making 0.054-inch bead-grommets was to wrap the wire for the required number of convolutions on a drum, and join the ends. The ring was then transferred to two sheaves on which it was rotated under tension, like a belt, to equalize the strands. Next it was wrapped with friction tape. Often, during the wrapping operation, the pressure of the tape turns would displace some of the strands. As a result, in the last few inches to be wrapped, one or more strands would project in the form of a hump. It was the general practice for the bead maker simply to push the humps down and continue wrapping. Thus the bead reinforcement, even though equalized by the sheave treatment, was unequalized by the taping operation and contained some strands that were understressed. It has been suggested that this may have been one of several reasons why this type of bead went out of style by 1940.

Another trouble arising from the 0.054-inch ferruled and similar beads was traceable to failure of the soldered joint. As a result of the bead's "working" in the normal operation of the tire, the soldered joint sometimes would fail, and one end of the wire would force its way through the bead fabric. As the tire continued to be driven, more and more of the bead wire would stick out.

Tales are told about motorists who, discovering the projecting wire, would wrap it around the wheel hub in order to get it out of the way. Then, at intervals, the driver would have to stop and wrap up more wire, until eventually he had transferred all of it from bead to hub. Finally, because of lack of reinforcement, the bead, and consequently the tire, would fail.

It is said that one motorist, discovering a short length of bead wire projecting through the outer rubber of his tire, thought it was some sort of lightning rod for conveying accumulated electrical charges to the ground!

One day the development department of a tire company received a 40- by 8-inch tire whose beads were reinforced with cables made from 0.054-inch wire. This tire was sent in because it "obviously" had developed a sand blister. But an autopsy revealed that, instead of sand, the blister contained all of the wire from one of the multiple cables, neatly coiled in a fleur-de-lis pattern.

In some foreign countries, bead-grommets were made similar to the 0.054-inch ferruled, but a heavier wire (0.070 or 0.072 inch) was used, and the ends were welded together. (See, also, ferruled bicycle-tire bead-grommets, pages 124 to 128.

1/16-INCH STRANDED REINFORCEMENTS

$\frac{1}{16}$-inch 6 by 7 Sash Cord (1911). A type of bead reinforcement known as the "$\frac{1}{16}$-inch 6 by 7 sash cord" was used for a relatively short time. The cord was of a variety commonly used for suspending window weights from sash, and was composed of a cotton center around which were wrapped six strands of seven wires each. The wires were soft iron, and each had a diameter of 0.007 inch. This cord was wound the required number of convolutions to form the bead-grommet; then its ends were taped (see Figure 2).

$\frac{1}{16}$-inch Seven-wire Strand (1911). The sash-cord bead-grommet was being tried by the B. F. Goodrich Company but was not considered satisfactory. Working with company technicians, J. C. DeGarmo, who then was with John A. Roebling's Sons Company, suggested the use of a seven-wire strand of 0.021-inch steel wire as a replacement for the sash cord. This was tried but was found to be too stiff (see Figure 3).

$\frac{1}{16}$-inch 19-wire Strand (1912). Next a 19-wire cable, consisting of six wires wrapped around a center wire, and, over that, 12 more wires wrapped in the opposite direction, was worked out. It proved to be satisfactory in beads. This reinforcement became known in the industry as the "Roebling 19-wire strand" and also as "$\frac{1}{16}$-inch beading strand." The wires were 0.011 inch in diameter and were of low-carbon steel. Up to eight layers, each consisting of from 1 to 15 wraps of 19-wire strand, were used in each bead. Thus a bead-grommet might consist of as many as 120 wraps, or 2,280 wires. The method of using this type of bead wire was essentially the same as that described for braided wire (page 72). In the early days, beads made with 19-wire strand were semicured. Later, a typical construction was to wrap the bead-grommet with cotton tape, run it through a cement box, let the cement dry, cold-press the bead-grommet assembly in a mold to produce a triangular cross section, and

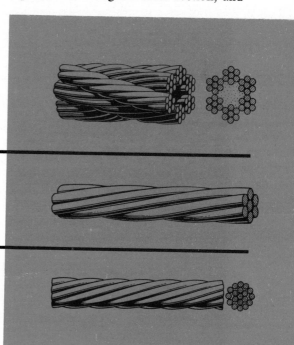

Figure 2.
Sash cord consisting of six strands of seven wires each, wrapped around a cotton center.

Figure 3.
Seven-wire strand tried experimentally in tires in 1911.

Figure 4.
Nineteen-wire strand, known also as 1/16-inch beading strand, introduced as a bead reinforcement in 1912.

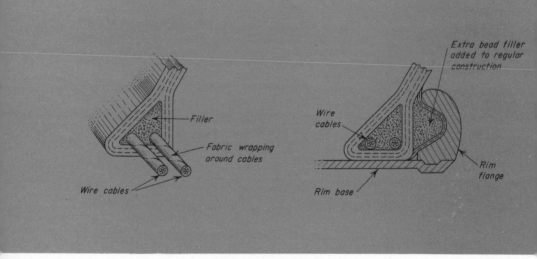

Figure 5. **Double-cable bead construction. Left: two five-wire cables in straight-side bead. Right: same bead construction modified for use on quick-detachable clincher rims.**

then build it into a tire. Some manufacturers ran the $\frac{1}{16}$-inch beading strand through a tuber to insulate it with rubber, then wound it into a ring-shaped reinforcement. Tensile strength of the beading strand (Roebling 19-wire strand) was around 272 pounds, with 260 pounds as the minimum (see Figure 4).

DOUBLE-CABLE BEADS

ONE OF THE SEVERAL ways of employing cables as bead reinforcements was exemplified by the Federal double-cable bead, which had come into use by 1913. It consisted of a pair of five-wire steel cables, each wrapped with fabric, surrounded by a filler of flexible rubber which, the makers claimed, was not as subject to cutting action as was the usual hard-rubber filler. The same cable rings were used in straight-side and quick-detachable clincher tires. The quick-detachable bead had extra filler and fabric added to the regular construction to form a clincher hook matching the rim-flange contour (see Figure 5).

GAMMETER TUBULAR BRAID (1916)

A BEAD REINFORCEMENT made of tubular wire fabric was developed by John R. Gammeter in 1916. A tubular braid somewhat greater in length than the circumference of the bead-grommet desired was provided with a core of unvulcanized hard rubber of lesser length. Ends of the tubular wire fabric were telescoped, like a snake swallowing its tail, until the ends of the rubber core came together. Rubber was applied to the outside of the braid, and over this a fabric cover was placed. Then the assembly was vulcanized in a mold to give it a triangular cross section. This bead never was used in production (see Figure 6).

0.011-INCH SINGLE LOW-CARBON WIRE (1918)

O NE RUBBER manufacturer attempted to save the stranding cost of $\frac{1}{16}$-inch 19-wire beading strand by using 19 single bright-finish low-carbon wires, 0.011 inch in diameter, in a bundle as a core. A tubular cotton cover was braided over this core, making the outside diameter somewhat larger without increasing the strength. Also, the resulting cable was much stiffer than the beading strand. The cable was put into production and wound on the bead former in exactly the same manner as the $\frac{1}{16}$-inch 19-wire beading strand. This construction was used less than a year and was replaced by the Pratt bead-grommet.

WELDED BEAD-GROMMET (1918–1920)

A T B. F. Goodrich, a welded-cable bead-grommet was introduced around 1918. The wire used was a low-carbon type, and sizes were as shown in the table below. The cable was formed by spiraling six wires around a single wire forming the core.

Cable Diameter, In.	Wire Diameter, In.
7/32	0.070
1/4	0.083
9/32	0.093
5/16	0.104

The cable ends were welded together, the joint buffed or ground to remove roughness and excess material, and the resulting ring put on a bulldozer (expanding machine) and stretched to exact size. This stretching operation produced a solid-bar effect on the cable, resulting in a relatively rigid bead. The stiffness was not excessive for fabric tires, which in themselves were quite rigid. But not long after the welded-cable bead-grommet was put into use, the cord tire entered the picture. A cord tire is more flexible than a fabric one, and requires a bead-grommet having greater flexibility than the welded-cable construction permitted. Cord-tire flexibility caused fatiguing stresses to concentrate in the welded joint of the bead wire, often resulting in breakage at that point. At one time, a metal sleeve was used: it was put over the weld in order to enable the bead-grommet to give longer service.

PRATT BEAD-GROMMET (1919–1928)

O NE OF the "most inextensible" bead reinforcements ever used was a multi-strand type known as the Pratt bead-grommet, Pratt cable, or Pratt bead ring, after its inventor A. C. Pratt. (A machine for winding the Pratt bead-grommet was patented by Robert C. Pierce.)

The Pratt cable was composed of seven wraps of a single wire, one forming the core and six being positioned spirally around it. The bead-grommet's outstanding feature was that both ends of the wire were inside

Figure 6.

Gammeter braid. Tubular bead reinforcement of braided wire. Splice was formed by having braid "swallow its tail" (patent 1,180,390).

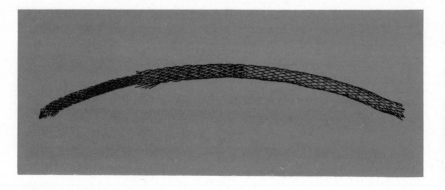

the spiral winding, so that there was no welded, brazed, or soldered joint. The wire ends were so firmly held by the outer strands that they could not slip or come loose. This construction was said to give a strength as much as 50 per cent greater than that achieved by comparable bead-grommet constructions.

The cable ring was made on a bead-grommet winding machine which included a ring winder carrying a spool of wire, and an annular form on which the wire was fed—the wire passing through a die, or quill, having a spiral passage to give it a permanent spiral form. The first turn of wire, forming the core of the bead-grommet, was made with the ring winder stationary, so that the wire issued from the die without twisting—as long as the wire was kept from turning on its own axis. Then, for the succeeding six turns, the ring winder was operated in the usual manner, the permanently spiraled wire being laid down in a neat, compact layer, about one twist in $2\frac{5}{8}$ inches. The final end of the wire was inserted between two outer strands and forced into position butted against the first end.

The cable ring then was removed from the winder and placed on an expanding machine (bulldozer). This machine applied an outward radial force well below the elastic limit of the wire but sufficient to expand the ring to exact size and shape, remove any kinks or irregularities in individual wires, and equalize the wires with respect to tension. The resulting bead-grommet had high tensile strength and virtually no stretch.

High-carbon steel was used for Pratt bead-grommets. For a $\frac{7}{32}$-inch diameter cable, 0.070-inch wire was used, and the expanded-ring tensile strength of the cable was around 8,000 pounds. For $\frac{1}{4}$-inch cable, 0.080-inch wire was used; and for $\frac{9}{32}$-inch cable, 0.090-inch wire. These

Figure 7.
The Pratt bead-grommet was a virtually endless ring-shaped cable. Ends of the wire were butted together in the center.

are almost the same wire sizes as those used in welded-cable bead-grommets of similar sectional diameter. However, the welded-cable ring was not so strong as the Pratt because of the weld and the difference in wire characteristics. Tensile strengths of the $\frac{7}{32}$-inch bead-grommets were: welded cable (of low-carbon wire), 2,800 pounds. Pratt cable (of high-carbon wire), 8,000 pounds.

There were several methods of handling a Pratt bead-grommet after it had been made. After being formed and expanded, each bead-grommet was cleaned either with benzol or Oakite, dried, and dipped into or rolled through rubber cement. The coated cable sometimes was installed in a tire without further treatment after drying—the various fabric plies of the tire being folded around it in a manner designed to hold it firmly in place. But a better method was to cover the cable ring with hard rubber and fabric: the rubber acted as a junction between the cable and the rest of the tire, and lessened the tendency of the bead fabric to tear itself loose from the wires.

The rubber compound, in the form of a ribbon whose width was equal to the sectional circumference of the cable, and whose length was equal to the circumference of the bead-grommet, was laid on a strip of bias-cut frictioned cotton fabric $1\frac{1}{4}$ inch or so wider than the rubber. The bead-grommet was rolled along to pick up the ribbon and strip. The rubber was compacted into a uniform layer, and the fabric was brought together to form a flipper which helped tie the bead-grommet into the rest of the tire structure when the cable was installed. A variation was to wrap the cable with rubberized fabric, place it in a bead-forming mold along with filler strips of rubber and a rubberized-fabric cover, and then transfer it to a ring-shaped mold of triangular section, for semicuring.

Although the cable was very strong, rigid, and free of "joint troubles," and although its strength could be easily calculated (being almost exactly seven times the strength of the individual wire since there was no welding or other heating operation to lower tensile characteristics), the Pratt ring gave way to other types of bead-grommets. In fact, in its strength lay the reasons for its downfall. The Pratt bead had absolutely no flexibility. It had to be made exactly to size. It was satisfactory in the fabric tire when made to size; but when it was used in the balloon tire, which had a cord construction that was more flexible than fabric construction, this particular type of bead proved too rigid and did not possess the flexibility required in the bead at the time the tire was being cured. The Pratt bead-grommet also was comparatively costly. The machines on which it was made were relatively slow. Around 1920, the cost of a complete $\frac{7}{32}$-inch Pratt-cable ring was about 17 cents, or 34 cents per tire.

PIERCE TAPE (INTRODUCED 1925)

$\mathcal{B}$ASICALLY, PIERCE TAPE is a series of parallel wires positioned side by side and held together by a smaller weft or filler wire woven back and forth in zigzag fashion. The main wires are of high-carbon steel, and the filler wire is of low-carbon steel. The filler wire holds the parallel wires together not only while they are being processed into a bead-grommet but also during the building and curing of the tire.

It became necessary to have very straight wire for the manufacture of this tape, because of the fact that any kinks or waves in the line wires would cause the tape to tip and be hard to handle. Therefore, methods had to be developed for making what is known as "super-straight" wire. This wire will lie dead on the floor without curving itself into a small circle, and it makes possible a satisfactory tape.

Pierce tape, named after Robert C. Pierce, who devised the method and machinery for making it, is manufactured solely by the National-Standard Company, and is normally made in widths ranging from 3 to 13 wires, the wire diameter being either 0.037 or 0.043 inch, as indicated in Figure 8.

Various Pierce-tape wire sizes and finishes were introduced as follows:

Wire Size, Finish	Year Introduced
0.035-in. tinned	1925
0.037-in. bronze plate	1928
0.037-in. AP-1 (zinc-copper)	1931
0.043-in. bronze plate	1931
0.043-in. AP-1	1932

During the placing of the filler wire in the manufacture of Pierce tape, the individual warp wires are fed through the machine under equal tension. Consequently, the bead-grommet made from this tape is composed of a series of wires which share the tensile load equally. The tape is customarily run through an insulating head to receive a coating of rubber compound. Then it is wound the required number of convolutions or turns on a bead former. Ends of the wire tape may be anchored to the rest of the bead-grommet by wrapping it with rubberized tape or by applying fasteners such as wire staples.

The tape is customarily made with either a B.P. (bronze plate) or an AP-1 (Avery Process No. 1) finish. The AP-1 finish is copper plate over

TAPE
.037" DIAMETER WIRE
Average tensile per strand — 305 lbs. (270,000 psi)

Strand	Wire Diameter	Pick	Max. Thickness	Total Tensile	Approx. Width	Wt. Per 1000 ft.
3	.037	1.25	.057	873	.170	11.90
4	.037	1.43	.057	1164	.200	15.65
5	.037	1.67	.065	1455	.240	19.70
6	.037	1.79	.068	1746	.265	23.00
7	.037	1.79	.073	2037	.310	26.50
8	.037	2.00	.073	2328	.330	30.00
9	.037	2.00	.073	2617	.360	35.40
10	.037	2.68	.077	2910	.390	38.50
11	.037	2.68	.077	3201	.420	40.50
12	.037	2.68	.077	3492	.455	44.10
13	.037	2.68	.077	3783	.500	49.80

TAPE
.043" DIAMETER WIRE
Average tensile per strand — 405 lbs. (270,000 psi)

Strand	Wire Diameter	Pick	Max. Thickness	Total Tensile	Approx. Width	Wt. per 1000 ft.
3	.043	1.43	.062	1173	.178	16.22
4	.043	1.67	.065	1564	.227	21.22
5	.043	1.67	.073	1955	.275	26.50
6	.043	1.79	.077	2346	.318	31.71
7	.043	2.00	.082	2737	.365	37.00
8	.043	2.00	.082	3128	.412	42.30
9	.043	2.00	.086	3519	.430	46.30
10	.043	2.68	.090	3910	.487	52.82

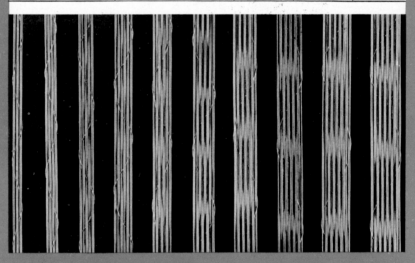

Figure 8. Pierce tape, from 3 to 12 strand.

a coating of zinc. During the vulcanizing process, a strong adhesive bond is formed between copper and rubber. The underlying zinc coating provides high resistance to corrosion. (See page 143 for further details of AP-1 finish.)

WEFTLESS BEADS (INTRODUCED 1929)

$\mathcal{T}$HE WEFTLESS bead reinforcement, a type still in use and adapted primarily to passenger-car, bus, and truck tires, consists of a number of 0.037-inch B.P. or AP-1 coated parallel wires held together by a coating of rubber, the wires being positioned side by side to form a ribbon or band one wire thick. This ribbon is wound on a bead former the required number of turns to produce the tensile strength needed in the bead-grommet. Thus, a four-wire weftless strip might make four convolutions to form a 4 by 4 bead-grommet (16 wires in a cross section). For several years, 0.043-inch wire having an AP-1 finish was used, but then was discontinued in favor of 0.037-inch wire, which has become the standard size for this construction.

Weftless bead-grommets are made in the rubber factory using them. Single wires of the required number are fed through the insulating head of a tubing machine, to emerge as a single unit consisting of the wires held together and covered by uncured rubber compound. This strip goes immediately to a bead machine that forms it into ring-shaped bead-grommets. The ends of the wire group may be simply overlapped a few inches without special fastening other than the cohesion of the rubber coating, or one or both ends may be wrapped with narrow tape. A recent tendency has been toward the use of one or two wire staples to clamp the wires near their ends, the staples forming close-fitting rings or bands around the wire bundle.

For making satisfactory weftless beads, a straight, high-tensile wire that is "dead" and thus has no tendency to coil is required. Because the wires are held together only by rubber compound during manufacture of this bead, they would, if not straight, make an imperfect bead-grommet.

Some approximate dates in the history of weftless beads are:

Wire Size and Type	Date Introduced (Approx.)
0.037-in. B.P. single weftless	1929
0.037-in. AP-1 single weftless	1931
0.043-in. AP-1 single weftless	1932

85

Weftless bead reinforcement is also known by such names as "Alder-fer," "Sterling," "fillerless," "multi-strand tape," "web tape," and "creel bead."

ABBOTT SINGLE-STRAND (INTRODUCED 1930)

*D*EVELOPMENT WORK was started in 1930 on a type of bead reinforce-ment that became known as the "Abbott wire" or "Abbott bead." By 1931 it had replaced the old 0.054-inch soldered and ferruled piano-wire bead.

Briefly, the manufacture of an Abbott bead has been described as fol-lows: From its reel a single wire moved through the insulating-head die of a tubing machine, and emerged with a coating of uncured rubber com-pound. In a continuous operation the rubber-covered wire was wound in annular form on a driven reel. After the desired number of convolu-tions had been wound, the wire was cut, and the ends forming the bead-grommet were overlapped about 1 inch.

Considerable advantage was claimed for the Abbott bead over the old 0.054-inch bare-wire construction. The eliminating of ferrules and of the soldering of the wire ends speeded the manufacturing process consider-ably. Other advantages cited by the proponents of this bead, in compari-son with other types of bead reinforcements, were that any number of wire convolutions could be obtained in a bead-grommet, and the single short overlap of wire created better balance with considerably less waste of tensile strength, as compared to a multiplicity of wires.

As a result of continuing development efforts, the machine for making the Abbott bead was greatly improved in the succeeding years.

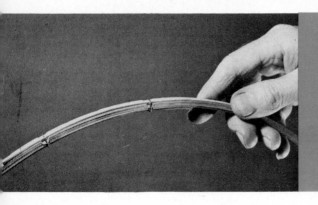

Figure 9.

Weftless bead-grommet for passenger-car tire, showing 6-inch overlap reinforced with two wire staples. The bead-grommet consists of five turns of four wires each.

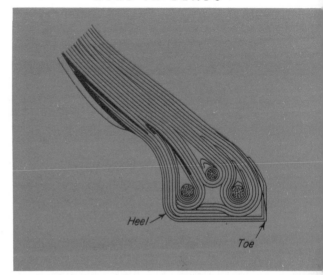

Figure 10.

Transportation-tire bead construction (1930). Three steel cables were used as a reinforcement, two being positioned toward heel and toe for stability.

MULTIPLE BEADS

*I*N AN effort to obtain great bead strength and stability, beads reinforced by as many as five steel-wire bead-grommets were developed. These were the forerunners of present-day dual and triple beads in tires made on undercut drums. A development considered by some tire men as a turning point in bead construction was the introduction of multiple beads having cord turn-ups and no flipper. Cord plies forming the tire carcass were brought around the bead-grommets and anchored by being turned up a short distance. Because there were several bead-grommets, only relatively few plies were wrapped around each one. This kept the thickness of fabric between the bead wire and the rim to a minimum, a construction intended to produce a high degree of stability.

Multiple beads are used in tires intended for severe service, such as those on trucks, airplanes, and earth-moving equipment.

PATENTS MENTIONED IN CHAPTER 5

Inventor	Patent	U.S.	Year
Gammeter, John	Tubular braid	1,180,390	1916
Pratt, A. C.	Bead grommet	1,294,160	1919
Pierce, Robert C.	Pratt-bead machine	1,415,696	1922

IMPORTANT DEVELOPMENTS IN HISTORY OF WIRE BEADS

(Some dates are approximate or uncertain)

Type of Bead Reinforcement	Year Introduced	Still in Use
Flat wire braid	1905	X
0.054-in. tinned high-carbon (piano wire)	1906	
0.072-in. tinned high-carbon	1906	
1/16-in. 6 by 7 sash cord (experimental)	1911	
1/16-in. seven-wire strand (experimental)	1911	
1/16-in. 19-wire strand	1912	
Federal double-cable bead	1913	
Tubular braid (Gammeter)	1916	
0.011-in. bright, single-wire, low-carbon, cotton braid	1918	
Welded-cable bead-grommet	1918	
Pratt bead-grommet	1919	
Pierce tape, 0.035-in. tinned wire	1925	
Pierce tape, 0.037-in. B.P. finish	1928	X
Pierce tape, 0.037-in. AP–1 finish	1931	X
Pierce tape, 0.043-in. B.P. finish	1931	
Pierce tape, 0.043-in. AP–1 finish	1932	
Single weftless 0.037-in. B.P. finish	1929	X
Single weftless 0.037-in. AP–1 finish	1931	X
Single weftless 0.043-in. AP–1 finish	1932	
Abbott bead, 0.037-in. wire	1930	X

CHAPTER 6 § BEAD MANUFACTURE

*I*N PRECEDING chapters, some details of bead manufacture have been mentioned. There are many other aspects to the process of combining wire, rubber, fabric, and perhaps other materials to form the beads of the typical pneumatic tire.

As in almost every field of industrial activity, there have been countless variations in the ways in which tires, and therefore tire beads, have been made. Even today, when the design and construction of beads have been more or less standardized, there is considerable difference in engineering opinion concerning almost every phase of the process: concerning such details as the amount of overlap of the wire reinforcement, the manner in which the fabric wrap should be applied to the bead-grommet, and so on. It is not possible to describe in detail here all the ways in which beads have been made, but some typical processes will be mentioned. It should be kept in mind that from the very beginning of bead history, each manufacturer has had his own favorite set of ideas and methods. This condition shows little sign of vanishing. So the processes described here should be considered as typical rather than specific or exceptional.

CLINCHER BEADS

*N*ONWIRE CLINCHER beads were made by extruding the rubber cores through a die and wrapping them with frictioned fabric. The cores were semicured to shape, either before or after being formed into endless rings.

Here is the process followed in one factory, as recalled by a veteran tire designer: The bead-core stock, a compound containing a considerable percentage of sulfur to make it hard, was shaped by extruding it with a tubing machine. The core was semicured in continuous lengths on a 15-foot gooseneck press. This press handled the cores in straight lengths, two dozen at a time. Next the core, now having a cross-sectional shape somewhat resembling that of a clincher hook, was buffed and dipped into or brushed with cement. When the cement had become dry, a strip of bias-cut square-woven frictioned fabric was applied along the surfaces that would lie toward the inner tube and rim base. Ends of the core were cut on an angle for splicing, and the fabric was similarly joined a short distance from the core splice. Then the bead was placed in a contour press and given a short second cure. Finally it was built into the tire, and received its third and final cure when the tire was vulcanized.

INTEGRAL BEADS

IT GENERALLY has been the practice to make beads as a separate unit and later to combine them with the main plies of fabric, tread, and other components of the tire. However, various tire makers have done differently. In the early days of pneumatics, bicycle tires sometimes were made with hollow beaded edges through which reinforcing wires were run after the tire had been cured. There were a lot of variations. Later, when machine building of tires had become the rule, a bicycle-tire machine which used the wire bead-grommets as a sort of form or drum on which to assemble the fabric and rubber plies was developed. This was the Healey-Shaw machine. The wire bead reinforcements were held in a parallel position, and bias fabric strips were run diagonally around and between them, forming the tire body. Other machines and methods were developed for putting the bead-grommets directly into the tire while it was being put together on a ring-shaped steel core (see the Morris, or Yoder, machine, Figure 14, page 119.) Later, the practice of making beads as separate units consisting of core, filler gum, cover, and flipper, and incorporating them into the carcass during the tire-building stage, was generally adopted.

Preformed Beads. Clincher beads, which contained no wire or other metallic reinforcement; quick-detachable beads, which contained reinforcements made of such materials as cotton fibers, cords, fabric strips, and wire; and, to some extent, straight-side beads, which were reinforced by wire strands, braid, etc., often were inclined to get out of round. So the practice of ironing out irregularities by pressing the uncured bead in a cold or heated mold was introduced. In the days preceding the perfection of modern chemical accelerators, beads had to be partially vulcanized before being combined with other elements of the tire carcass, and this, also, helped to hold them in shape until they were installed.

Positioning Beads. After a bead is shaped, it has to be positioned with considerable accuracy with respect to the plies forming the sidewall of the tire, or the tire will not be true in shape, and operational trouble may develop eventually. In earlier days, various holders, gauges, and similar gadgets were devised for positioning beads. But often the placing of a bead was guided by a line drawn around the sidewall of the carcass by the tire builder: he simply held a piece of chalk against the tire while rotating the ring core on which it was being built. On a modern tire-building machine, the beads are placed in holders which swing them accurately into position when the carcass is ready to receive them.

Bead Shapes. The bead in a straight-side tire is generally more or less triangular in cross section; and so it was at one time considered essential that the bead be of that shape before it was installed. In the case of clincher beads, composed of semihard rubber compound and fabric, the rubber bead core might be extruded as a round rod; but subsequent operations usually converted it approximately into its final shape before it reached the tire.

Semicuring. Before modern chemical accelerators were developed, the rate of vulcanization in different regions of a tire could not be controlled

Figure 1.
Wrapped and flipped bead-grommets on bead-placing ring of a modern tire-building machine.

adequately by varying the rubber compound. If the rubber parts of a tire, bead and all, were composed of uncured compound, heat penetration into the bead would not be sufficient, with the accelerators then used, to cure the bead stock completely by the time the rest of the tire was fully vulcanized. As a result, the bead would be undercured and would be lacking in durability. So it became the practice to semicure all beads before they were installed. This continued through the era of the clinchers and quick-detachables and into the straight-side period—until about the time the cord tire began to take hold. The bead cores, either before or after being wrapped with fabric, were placed in a mold and heated under temperature-time conditions that would cure the rubber compound enough to enable it to become fully vulcanized later when the entire tire was cured. Sometimes a bead would be given two partial cures before being installed in a tire, as already mentioned (page 89). This pre-cooking of tire beads was comparable to the way a cook makes some types of pies: she shapes the crust and places it in the oven for a time. Then she adds the filling, and completes the baking. Without the pre-baking, the crust would be underdone and probably soggy in the bottom.

With the perfection of improved chemical accelerators which, when mixed in rubber compounds, speed and control their rates of vulcanization, semicured beads began to pass into history. Today the bead stock is compounded so it will vulcanize more rapidly than that in other parts of the tire. As a result, the entire tire can be cured at once and in a lot less time than in the days of semicured beads and inferior accelerators. (Culinary note: maybe piecrust accelerators will be developed some day!)

WIRE BEADS

Insulation. Since the adoption of wire as a reinforcement in straight-side tire beads, there have been different opinions among tire engineers on the matter of bead insulation. This insulation, sometimes called bead stock, is the rubber compound that surrounds the wire. It has several purposes: It helps anchor the wires in place. It acts as a cushion between wires, thus reducing or preventing metal-to-metal contact and resultant wear. It acts as a medium for joining the wire reinforcement to the surrounding fabric and rubber. It is of help in processing the bead to the desired cross-sectional shape. During manufacture, the rubber insulation holds the wires in position and often prevents the bead-grommet from unwinding before the tire is cured.

Tire engineers have differed over such details as the ratio of gum stock to wire in the bead, and whether or not each wire should be isolated by being surrounded with rubber so that it floats alone in the bead structure. Some prefer to place the wires in a compact, cablelike bundle. As a happy medium, there is a third group of technicians who care little whether or not the wires touch each other. But all of them seem to agree that no matter what the arrangement of wires in a bead, there should be ample insulating rubber between the metal and the cotton jacket or cover surrounding it.

Insulating Wires. A number of methods have been developed for getting the rubber compound around the wires. Included among these are:

1. LAMINATING. Strips of uncured hard rubber were placed over each turn of wire reinforcement as it was wound on the bead-grommet former. For example, in making a bead from flat wire braid, a workman might lay the first turn down on a skim coating of rubber applied to fabric. Over this turn he next placed a strip of uncured hard rubber. Then he wound another turn of braid, placed another strip of rubber, and so on until the required number of convolutions were in place. Finally he wrapped the bead-grommet in fabric which might be friction-coated, or might be the strip on which the first turn was laid and which bore the skim coat that would supply additional rubber to the bead insulation. When a bead built up in this manner was heated, either during the semi-curing or the tire-vulcanizing stage, the laminating rubber compound, plus any skim coating involved, would soften and flow together to form a homogeneous mass which, ideally, surrounded every wire.

2. SKIM-COATED COVER. The wire bead-grommet was cleaned, coated with cement, dried, and wrapped with fabric bearing on one surface a skim coating of uncured rubber. The thickness of this skim coat was controlled so it provided enough gum to flow, during the vulcanizing period, around all the wires and thus insulate them.

3. TUBED WIRES. This is the method most widely used today. The steel reinforcement, in the form of a single wire, grouped strands (weftless), flat wire braid, or Pierce tape, is run through an insulating head attached to a tubing (rubber extruding) machine, and emerges with a uniform coating of uncured rubber compound. It is then wound into a bead-grommet. In the earlier years of tubed bead wire, the compound would be semicured after the bead had been formed and wrapped; but today the bead is built into the tire before any curing is done.

4. UNINSULATED WIRES. Some tire makers did not use any insulation for their bead wire other than the rubber and fabric that made up the plies of the bead portions of the tire. They would, for example, clean

a cable-type bead-grommet, roll it through or dip it into rubber cement, hang it up to dry until the cement was tacky, and then build the bead-grommet directly into the tire.

5. WRAPPED TUBING. A method used abroad, chiefly for airplane tires and special sizes, consists of running a single wire through a machine that folds a strip of rubber around it, the strip edges butting to form a seam. A bead-grommet is composed of from 10 to 30 turns of such rubber-covered wire, the ends being welded together. The bead-grommet is wound with fabric to which has been applied a fibrous rubber compound.

OVERLAPPING OF WIRES

WHEN A bead-grommet is made by winding wire around a former to produce a number of turns or convolutions, there always are two ends to be anchored in some manner. The amount these ends are overlapped and the method used for fastening them are two points on which technicians have not always agreed.

In bead-grommets made by winding a single uninsulated wire around and around, the wire ends often were fastened by twisting them together, slipping metal ferrules over the twist, and soldering. It was largely because of the soldering operation that tinned wire was used, although the adhesion between rubber and tin is practically nil. In the Pratt-cable bead-grommet, the wire ends were butted and neatly buried beneath the outer spiraled strands. In other constructions, ends were brazed or welded. Still another practice, when rubber-insulated wire is used, is to depend entirely on the rubber to hold the wire ends in place during the manufacturing process and, later, in the finished tire. Wire staples or tape wrappings often are used to assist the rubber in holding ends in position during manufacture.

In bead-grommets made of flat wire braid, Pierce tape, and weftless parallel wires, a coating of rubber is first applied. Then the braid, tape, or wire bundle is wound the required number of turns around the bead former, plus usually a few inches of overlap. Different tire technicians seem to have different ideas about the overlap, but for a long period the standard has been around 6 inches. However, some bead-grommets are made without any overlap at all, or with only a negligible amount, and with no special fastening at ends.

Determining Amount of Overlap. Tests to determine how much the overlap should be on wire that was not soldered were initially made on flat wire braid. One of the first machines devised for making static tests on the bead of a tire consisted of a special head installed on an Olsen tensile-testing machine, initially for the purpose of stretching and testing Pratt beads. This was at Erie, Pennsylvania, in 1919. Before the Olsen machine had been equipped with this special head, tests generally were made by stretching the bead between two pulleys. This distorted the bead, which in those days was very hard, so such tests were not very satisfactory.

When the Olsen testing machine was moved from Erie, where the Pratt bead had been developed, to the National-Standard Company plant at Niles, Michigan, it was put in use immediately to determine what the overlap should be on beads made from braided wire. That was before the days of the weftless and Pierce-tape types of beads. In the case of braid, the adhesion at that time was all mechanical. It was found, by means of the Olsen-machine tests, that a lap of braid of from 3 to 4 inches was sufficient to utilize the full strength of the bead.

When Pierce tape came along, the same testing program was arranged. Practically every tire company sent beads to the National-Standard plant, along with engineers to make the tests. Considerable variation was found in Pierce tape because of the differences in rubber compounds that were used to insulate it, and because of the differences in chemical adhesion between such compounds and the wire. Some companies felt that as much as a half turn around the bead was necessary, while others were satisfied with laps as short as 6 inches. There was, therefore, no standard adopted by all companies, for each one had its own convictions. Similar variations have developed with respect to weftless bead reinforcements.

Wrapping Ends. An overlapped joint is not wholly efficient if one or both ends of the braid, tape, or other element forming the bead-grommet can get out of line. An end that projects can be a nuisance when the bead-grommet is being handled during manufacturing operations. So, early in the history of wire in beads, it became the practice to wrap something around the ends to hold them in place, at least until the bead-grommet could be incorporated into the tire. Friction tape was used in most cases and for a long time was applied by hand. About 1927, engineers developed an automatic wrapping machine for taping the ends in bead-grommets made from flat wire braid and Pierce tape. This machine was faster and more uniform than skilled hand wrappers. Some manufacturers adopted the practice of spirally wrapping the entire overlapped portion of the bead-grommet to hold the two ends in place.

Another method, which was tried years ago and was again in use in the early 1950's, is to install one or two wire staples so they encircle the

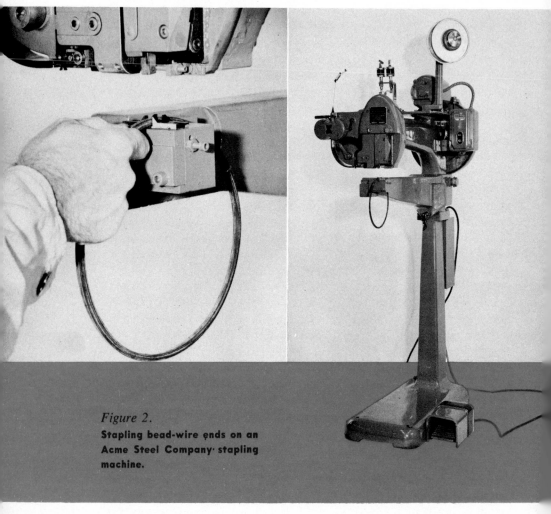

Figure 2.
Stapling bead-wire ends on an Acme Steel Company· stapling machine.

bundles of bead wires to fasten the ends in place. When two staples are used on a 6-inch overlap, each is placed about $1\frac{1}{4}$ inches from a wire end. When a shorter overlap and a single staple are used, the staple is positioned about midway between ends. The fasteners are placed by stapling machines as an operation immediately following removal of the ring from the bead former.

According to some tire technicians, elimination of the overlap in a bead-grommet reduces the over-all strength of the bead-grommet to the extent of one complete convolution. In other words, the bead-grommet then has a 360-degree overlap and has, in effect, lost one turn of wire, tape, or braid.

After a bead of present-day construction has been cured, the rubber surrounding the wires does practically all the work of holding them in place. Staples, wrappings of tape or cord, and other fastening devices are considered primarily useful for holding the ends in place during manufacture.

Bead-grommet Cover. Generally it has been the practice to apply a cover to the bead core for the purpose of providing better adhesion between the core and surrounding fabric plies. Cotton fabric impregnated with rubber has been used almost universally. Frictioned fabric contains uncured rubber that has been forced into it by rollers (the machine used now being known as a calender). In the early days the tire maker followed the practice of laying a strip of uncured rubber on a strip of frictioned fabric, which then was wrapped around the bead-grommet with the rubber inside to become the insulation for the wire. As this practice continued, the art of applying the skim coat of uncured rubber to the fabric with rollers or a calender was developed. Later, as the industry learned how to rubber-cover or insulate the wires before they were wound to form a bead-grommet, it was no longer necessary to apply this extra coat of rubber to the fabric bead covering. However, some manufacturers have continued to use a moderated skim coat, believing it to be a safety measure.

Applying Cover. The bead cover usually is applied in one of two ways: (1) Square-woven friction tape ¾-inch or so wide is wrapped spirally around the bead-grommet, which is made of rubber-insulated wire strands, braid, or tape. This is done by a machine which is adjusted to position the wraps so that edges butt, overlap, or are a fraction of an inch apart—depending on the manufacturer's ideas of how such a wrap should be applied. (2) A strip of square-woven frictioned fabric is wrapped circumferentially around the ring-shaped bead-grommet, and its edges are brought around and overlapped. This is done on a bead-wrapping machine whose folders and rollers press the tacky fabric into complete contact with the bead core. Machines were used for wrapping the old clincher beads, either cured or uncured.

In the period when beads were semicured, the fabric wrapping lost part of its initial tackiness during the first curing cycle. Therefore it was buffed to roughen its surface and then coated with rubber cement so it would adhere to the surrounding plies of the tire.

Flipping. As described in connection with the Pratt cable (page 82), bead-grommets were cleaned, coated with cement, wrapped with a layer

97

Figure 3.
A late type of bead spiral-wrapping machine (1950).

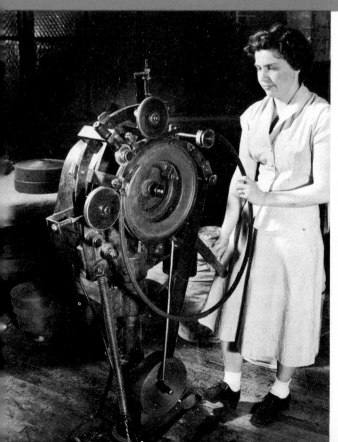

Figure 4.
Jacket-wrapping a tire bead.

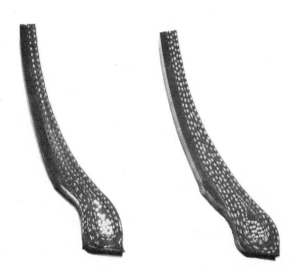

Figure 5.

Cross sections of beads. Right: bead-grommet with wire ends properly held in place. Left: bead-grommet exhibiting wire movement into bead apex because of improper fastening of ends.

of uncured rubber, then with a layer of frictioned fabric, and finally with a second fabric strip whose edges were pinched together to form a projecting skirt that would help hold the bead core in position among other plies of the carcass. The use of such a fabric skirt became general practice in tire building. The strip forming it is known as a bead "flip," and its application to the bead as "flipping."

The flipper strip was used on clincher beads, and machines were developed for applying it. Essentially, wrapping and flipping a bead are the same. The wrap is a fabric cover applied with a smooth seam, while the flipper is a fabric cover, usually applied over the wrap, whose edges project at an angle to form an annular skirt. Machines for applying flipper strips employ folding devices and rollers to guide the rubber-impregnated fabric into place.

Before a flipper is applied to a wrapped bead, a strip of gum is placed around the outer circumference of the bead-grommet—again with the aid of a machine—to fill the triangular space above the bead. This space is bounded by the bead-grommet and the two converging surfaces of the flipper fabric. This filler in the apex of the bead is known primarily as the "bead-gum neck."

The flipper strip may be composed of more than one ply of fabric. In

Figure 6.
Bead-flipping machine in operation.

Figure 7 (opposite).
Bead-flipping machine used in Europe in 1927.

a two- or three-ply strip, the plies are assembled before going to the machine, and all are flipped at once. Edges of the flipper plies are stepped in the manner required by the tire design. The stepping or staggering of ply laps in the flipper, together with the similar distribution of plies making up the remainder of the bead structure, tends to prevent excessive flexing of the bead. The action is very much like that of a leaf spring: the center of the spring, containing more leaves, is flexed much less than the ends, which, through the stepped-down arrangement, involve only a few leaves. In a tire, a considerable number of ply thicknesses make up the bead portions of the carcass; but because of the stepped arrangement of plies, relatively few thicknesses are found in the sidewalls. Therefore flexing forces are diverted from the beads to sidewalls, where the movements they cause can do little or no harm.

Besides helping to divert flexing forces, the bead flipper is the means of tying the bead-grommet into the ply structure of the tire. The bead skirt is positioned at such an angle that it matches the contour of the tire carcass on the building drum. Skirt width is determined by the design of the tire.

Crimped Flipper. Because there is a considerable difference in the circumference of the flipper when measured at the inner circumference of the bead-grommet and at the outer margin of the skirt (except when the skirt projects at an angle of 90 degrees with respect to the plane of the bead-grommet ring), the introduction of balloon tires created a flipper problem. Stretching of the flipper skirt in the balloon tire would cause unwanted strain in the thin sidewalls. So a crimper flipping machine was devised. It has a pair of gears between which the fabric is fed. This shortens the center portion of the strip by tucking or crimping it so that it will match more nearly the circumference of the bead-grommet, while the circumference at the skirt margin remains approximately as large as that of the sidewalls. The use of bias-cut fabric for flipper strips further minimizes the strain in flipper skirt and sidewall.

The covering and flipping steps can be varied to match the bead core construction. Thus when single-strand wire was wound into a ring without being rubber-coated, the bead-covering machine applied a fabric carrying a skim coat of gum. Likewise, when uninsulated wire braid was being used for the bead-grommet, a wrapping having a skim coat nearly

0.100 inch thick was applied, followed by a flipper strip. But when the braid is run through a tuber which applies rubber insulation, the wrap is composed of frictioned fabric without skim coating.

Tires having no flippers have been, and are at this time, being made. Cord plies of the tire carcass are brought down around the wire bead and then extended upward into the sidewall of the tire to form a reinforcement, commonly referred to as a "high turn-up."

CHAPTER 7 § MACHINES FOR BEAD
MANUFACTURE

*A*LMOST AS SOON as the pneumatic tire appeared, inventors began to devise ways of making its various elements on machines instead of by hand. Clincher-bead cores were formed by forcing rubber compound through the die of an extruding machine; and various devices were developed for wrapping the core with rubber-impregnated fabric, forming the bead ring, molding it into the desired sectional shape, precuring it, and centering it on the casing during the tire-building stage.

When the quick-detachable tire was introduced, a new crop of bead-making machines appeared. These were used for forming inextensible beads of rubberized cord, strips of rubber-impregnated fabric, and so on. The Stevens bead-forming machine tore wide strips of frictioned fabric into narrow strips and then combined and shaped them to form a bead core. Another machine wound string into a groove previously lined with frictioned fabric; the fabric edges then were folded to form an envelope covering the string.

The straight-side tire, with its wire-reinforced beads, brought new problems for the machine designers. The easiest way to transform a single wire, group of wires, wire braid, or wire tape into a ring-shaped bead-grommet is to wind it around a circular form. And so the heart of practically all bead-making machines has been (and is) some sort of wheel whose rim is grooved or otherwise shaped to permit wire to be wound on it. Some of the various methods are described in the following paragraphs.

Handwheel. One of the first wire-bead machines was the simple hand-wheel. This consisted of a wheel mounted on a stand so that it could be rotated by hand in a vertical plane. The wheel rim was grooved to receive the bead wire, the groove or rabbet being L-shaped so the bead-grommet could be removed after having been formed. The operator placed a frictioned-fabric cover around the groove, fastened the end of the bead wire or braid in a slot in the wheel, turned the wheel by means of a hand crank until the desired number of wire convolutions had been wound, stopped the wheel, and snipped the wire in two with a hand cutting tool. Next he folded the fabric over to complete the cover, forced the bead ring off the wheel with a "turnover tool" resembling a screw driver, and then started the cycle again. The handwheel bead winder was used extensively, and a skilled operator could achieve good production speed on it. Handwheels were in use in a number of plants up to a few years ago for turning out odd-sized beads in limited quantities and for experimental work; and it is not unlikely that some of these machines can be found still in occasional operation.

Banner Bead Machine. It was logical that someone should motorize the handwheel to speed production. Typical of the machines into which this evolved was the original Banner bead-making machine, which was introduced around 1922. It had a bead former, or wheel, driven through a system of gears by a motor. After each bead-grommet had been formed, the wire was cut by hand. In 1928, the old Banner bead machine was redesigned and became the first clutch-operated universal bead-winding machine. It was semiautomatic. The operator placed the end of the wire braid in a gap on the bead former (wheel), stepped on a foot pedal to start the former rotating, and the machine wound the required number

Figure 1.
Original Banner bead machine, built about 1922.

Figure 2 (opposite).
Goodyear horizontal chuck arrangement for making bead-grommets.

of convolutions and stopped automatically. Pressure on another foot control actuated an air-driven knife, which cut the braid. The bead-grommet was removed, and the cycle repeated. In 1937 a fully automatic cutoff and wire-advance attachment was perfected, adaptable to older Banner machines as well as new ones.

The improved Banner machine introduced a new flexibility into the making of bead-grommets. For each bead-grommet size, there was a former; and changing from one size to another required only 2 minutes or so and the loosening and tightening of a setscrew. The increasing or reducing of the number of fabric plies between the bead-grommet and the rim would require slight changes in grommet diameters, and each former was adjustable so that fractional requirements could be handled. Such changes were made possible by gauge plates which controlled the precise diameters of the formers. Each plate was held in place by two bolts; and it was stamped with the corresponding bead diameter.

Another motor-driven bead winder, called the Gillette, had a segmented, expandable former on which the wire was wound. The segments could be adjusted for precise bead-grommet size and could be contracted momentarily for removal of finished bead-grommets.

Goodyear Horizontal Chuck. Various tire manufacturers, at different times, developed their own methods of making bead-grommets. For a number of years, bead-grommets were made by the Goodyear Tire & Rubber Company on a horizontal power-driven chuck, or former, having

a right-angled groove or ledge around the outer edge, much like that on the old handwheel. When flat wire braid was used, it was first run through an insulating machine which coated it with uncured rubber compound and then was stored on a reel, with a strip of herringbone-weave cotton tape between turns to keep them from sticking to each other. Eventually the reel would be placed on a stand, equipped with a brake, for feeding the braid to the bead-making unit.

The insulated wire was led from the reel through a hand-operated guide and stitcher mounted on the bead-maker frame and wound around the right-angled ledge. This ledge previously had been covered with bias-cut, friction-coated fabric to form the wrap or flipper. The guide-stitcher was used to force the turns into place—so many turns "down," so many "up," and so many "diagonal." The resulting bead-grommet was triangular in shape. A filler of rubber was placed on the winding before the diagonal turns were applied, to form the core of the triangle. After the braid had been wound and cut, edges of the fabric cover were folded to form an overlapping seam and compacted with a hand stitcher, which then generally was used as a pry tool to force the bead-grommet off the chuck. The bead-grommet was semicured in a mold to triangular shape. Later, uncured beads were made in the same manner, until Pierce tape was adopted. Bead-grommets were made of the tape on the same machine, but all turns were in the "down" position.

Andrews Bead Machine. Similar to the Banner bead winder was the Andrews bead-making machine developed by Goodyear engineers. It had an automatic counting device which determined the number of convolutions in a bead-grommet. This made a clicking noise as it operated, and it sometimes gave the impression that the operator was determining the number of turns by counting clicks. A foot-controlled knife was used to cut the wire after the bead-grommet had been formed. This machine wound from two to eight convolutions. A different former was used for each bead diameter.

Model 46. The Banner bead winder was further refined and became the "Model 46." This machine, driven by a 1-horsepower motor, makes beads ranging in diameter from 3 to 40 inches, and having from two to twelve wraps (convolutions or turns). Model 46 is semiautomatic. It automatically wraps a predetermined number of convolutions on the bead former and stops. Then the bead wire is cut off by an air-operated knife, and the end of the wire is advanced for the start of another bead-grommet. To remove the finished bead-grommet, the operator depresses

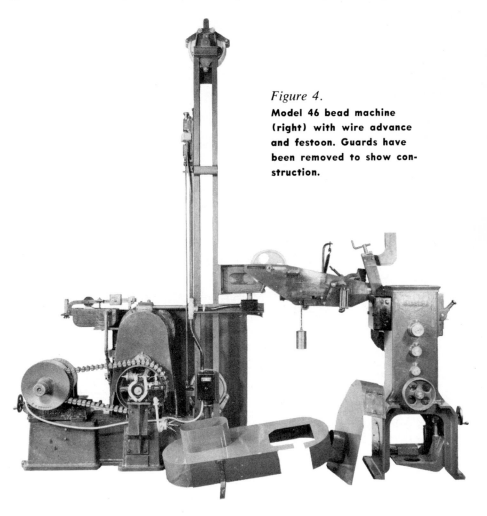

Figure 4.

Model 46 bead machine (right) with wire advance and festoon. Guards have been removed to show construction.

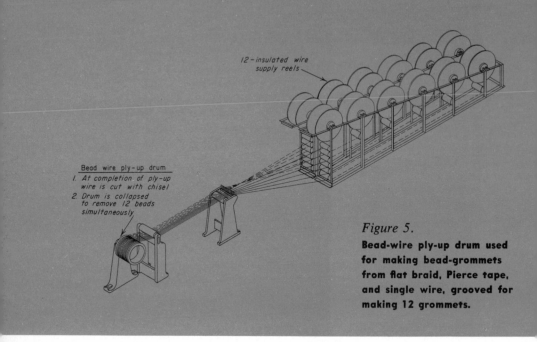

12 - insulated wire supply reels

Bead wire ply-up drum
1. At completion of ply-up wire is cut with chisel
2. Drum is collapsed to remove 12 beads simultaneously

Figure 5.

Bead-wire ply-up drum used for making bead-grommets from flat braid, Pierce tape, and single wire, grooved for making 12 grommets.

a foot-treadle air valve, which causes the gripper to release the bead and a section of the former to fold inward. Next he inserts the advanced end of the wire into the gripper. To close the former for the next bead, he operates a hand control. An air control is not used here because of the hazard of getting fingers caught in the mechanism during the closing cycle. After closing the former, the operator presses a foot switch to start the machine.

The Model 46 machine has an automatic convolution counter which, by moving a ratchet handle to the proper graduation, is adjusted for the number of wraps desired.

The automatic cutoff and wire advance cannot be used when making beads less than 6 inches in diameter. Finished bead-grommets are removed by hand after the former wire gripper has been opened. Formers are adjustable within approximate limits of 1 inch under and 1½ inches over the nominal bead circumference. A sizing link, properly stamped to indicate precise bead size, holds the former in adjustment. Formers smaller than twelve inches in diameter have to be opened by hand instead of air.

Bead-wire Ply-up Drum. For making bead-grommets of flat wire braid, there was developed by the Mason Tire and Rubber Company, and later improved by The B. F. Goodrich Company, a bead-grommet machine whose bead former was a collapsible drum having 12 circumferential grooves. This machine was used later for tape and also single wire. Each

Figure 6.

Bead former of redesigned Abbott machine. The wire was wound on a series of spirally-grooved pins, or flights, which rotated in unison to deliver the finished bead-grommet. The wire was cut without stopping the machine.

groove was wide enough to receive the braid or tape. The drum diameter measured at the groove bottom was the same as the desired inside diameter of the bead-grommet. The wire braid or tape, insulated with rubber, was stored on reels, one for each groove to be filled.

The operator would insert each braid or tape end into a gripper slot at the bottom of its respective groove. When all ends were attached, he would start the drum, which would revolve until the required number of convolutions, usually three or four, were wound into the grooves. Then the drum would stop automatically. Next the operator would place a steel bar under the strips of braid or tape and, with a chisel and hammer, rapidly cut each one. He made the cuts so there would be a 6-inch overlap of ends. Finally, he collapsed the drum and removed the bead-grommets, which were then ready for taping of the cut ends and for subsequent operations. The operator started the next cycle by inserting the braid or tape ends into the drum slots. A man could turn out a surprising number of bead-grommets on this machine.

Abbott Machine. The Abbott bead-winding machine, whose development started about 1930, used a single wire and formed the bead-grommet by winding this wire many times around a segmented former. Bead-grommet diameter was controlled by screws which moved the eight segments in or out. The former had to be stopped for cutting the wire each time a bead-grommet was completed.

Around 1933 or 1934, the Abbott machine was redesigned. A major improvement was the use of a former having a series of spirally grooved pins, or "flights," projecting from a slotted plate. The pins, which formed a circle, could be adjusted in the radial slots of the plate to control the diameter of the bead-grommet. As a bead-grommet was completed, the pins rotated, the grooves in them acting as screw threads to move the bead-grommet outward and off the former. At the same time, the wire

Figure 7.
FSW bead-winding machine. Finished bead coming off.

Figure 8.
Left: FSW bead-winding machine. Right: festoon unit.

was cut automatically. Production was continuous, the machine not stopping for wire cutoff. (See also Chapter 5, page 86.)

The FSW Machine. In 1930, engineers connected with the National Rubber Machinery Company, who had had a great deal to do with various kinds of equipment for manufacturing tires, evolved the idea that it might be possible to eliminate the bead department in a tire plant. This they proposed to do by incorporating the bead directly into the tire during the tire construction—an idea not strictly new, but one which never had been applied successfully to mass tire production. The development along this line did not prove to be practical; but out of the work came a very fine method of much faster bead building than had been accomplished before. This method was centered in a machine to which the name "FSW" was applied, this alphabetical designation being formed of the first letter of the name of each of the men who were in charge of this development—Frank, Shook, and White.

As the development on this machine progressed, patents were applied for; and it was found that patents covering the Andrews process, as previously described (page 107), dominated the machine. Arrangements were made, however, to market the machine; and it has now become what might be termed the universal bead-building machine in all tire plants. It is an automatic bead winder; and at the time this is being written, improvements are being designed which undoubtedly will increase its speed.

The FSW machine will make bead-grommets from 13 to 24 inches in diameter which have from two to eight convolutions or layers of fabricated wire (tape, braid, or weftless). The machine can be adjusted to give a lap of 3 to 9 inches.

The rubber-insulated bead wire is wound into a ring on a former, the starting end being gripped automatically and the wire being cut automatically at the finish of the winding. A different former is required for each rim diameter, the change from one size to another being accomplished by the removing and replacing of two cap screws. Each former is adjustable for fractional variations in bead-grommet size, and the adjustment is maintained by means of detachable links. These links are supplied in blank form to be drilled and stamped by the user. Instead of a set of fixed links, one company uses a micrometer arrangement to adjust the former until its diameter matches that of a gauge ring encircling the circumference on which the wire is to be wound.

Normally, formers less than 18 inches in diameter are machined $\frac{1}{4}$ inch over the base diameter of the rim, and formers larger than 18 inches are machined $\frac{1}{2}$ inch over the base diameter. Adjustment of formers less than 18 inches in diameter ranges from 0.180 to 0.800 inch over rim diameter; and adjustment of formers 18 inches and larger ranges from 0.400 to approximately 1.000 inch over nominal rim diameter.

Bead-on-edge Machine. In the 1930's a machine was developed for making preturned, or "on-edge," bead-grommets of braid only. It was operated for several years at an Akron rubber company plant. It handled only flat wire braid, and wound the convolutions edgeways—that is, with the flat surface of the braid parallel to the plane of the bead former. Thus the diameter of all convolutions was the same, as compared with the usual arrangement in which the diameter of each turn is greater than that of the preceding one. Also, a lower bead height could be obtained in a given width, a condition considered desirable because a low, wide bead is less likely to rock and is otherwise more stable. When the tire was shaped after being built on a drum, the on-edge bead-grommet adjusted itself better than other constructions because of the uniformity of the diameters of individual turns. By using more rubber on the braid edge that was to turn toward the apex of the bead, a natural gum neck was formed, eliminating the extra operation of applying a gum neck. This bead was used mostly in passenger and light truck tires.

BEAD-MAKING SYSTEM

A MODERN bead-making system includes the following machines or units:

1. The reel of wire braid or tape, or several reels of single-strand wire.

2. An insulating head attached to a standard tubing (rubber-extruding) machine.

3. A pull-off and festooner.

4. The bead-winding machine.

5. A bead-wrapping or cover machine.

6. A bead-flipping machine.

When tape or braid is being used, only a single reel with one stand is required; and the same is true when an Abbott-type bead is being made from a number of turns of single wire. When a weftless or fillerless bead is being made by running several parallel wires through the insulator, a reel and stand are required for each wire. Reel stands are equipped with

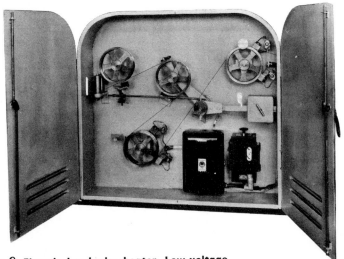

Figure 9. **Electric bead-wire heater. Low-voltage high-amperage current is fed to right-hand and bottom sheaves. The wire running between them forms part of the circuit and becomes heated because of its resistance.**

brakes or drags to prevent the reels from continuing to turn after tension on the wire is relieved. When single wires are being pulled from several reels simultaneously, it is necessary that the tension on all wires be equal. So a reel brake has been devised that works only when the wire running from reel to pull-off drum is slack.

When making weftless beads, an important unit is the gathering device positioned between the let-off and tuber. In order to avoid excessive wear on the insulating baffle, this device should not be less than 6 feet from the tuber and must be properly aligned with it. The reels of wire are fanned out and, to avoid abrupt angles, are placed some distance from the gathering device. The wires, entering the gatherer at various angles, are diverted to parallel paths so they will go through the insulating head in side-by-side positions. A preferred form of gathering unit consists of three steel rolls about 3 inches in diameter, one placed in a horizontal position, the others vertical. Wires pass first over the horizontal roll. When wire braid or Pierce tape is being processed, a guide having a single grooved roll or wheel is positioned 18 inches from the insulating head, and the let-off is placed so its reel center is 6 feet from the guide.

The insulating head applies a coating of uncured rubber compound to the single wire, tape, braid, or group of wires. Because the rubber will adhere better to the wire when the latter is heated, the wire usually is passed from the reel through a preheater before it enters the insulating-die head.

One arrangement for heating consists of a gas burner placed beneath the wire at a point just before it enters the tuber die. The flame is controlled by a magnetic valve wired into the pull-off motor circuit so the gas will be shut off when the motor stops. A small pilot flame ignites the burner when the motor starts.

Another preheating setup employs electricity and includes four guide rolls or grooved wheels. A low-voltage high-amperage current is fed to two of these wheels through brushes bearing against collector rings. The wheels are insulated from each other except when bead wire is running over them. The current, passing through the segment of wire extending from one wheel to the other, heats it. Current is adjusted to match the wire's resistance and rate of movement. When the wire stops, the heating current is shut off automatically, the transformer being controlled by the pull-off motor switch. Of course, the wire should not be heated enough to destroy its hardness characteristics.

Steam has been used for preheating bead wire but has given way in many plants to other methods. The steam unit consisted of a steel cabinet containing two drums over which the wire was fed; they held a total of 70 feet. Steam at low pressure was admitted to the top of the cabinet, surrounding and heating the wire on the drums. Any moisture that remained on the wire as it entered the insulating head was removed by the wiping action of the rubber compound at the baffle opening. When steam is used for preheating bead wire, there is no danger of overheating, no matter how long the pull-off is stopped. Steam also has a cleansing action that removes grease and other foreign material from wire.

Tubing Machine. The insulating head is a device for applying a coating of uncured rubber compound to a single wire or a combination of wires. It is mounted on a rubber-extruding or tubing machine having a worm or screw, like that in a sausage grinder, which forces the insulating compound along a tubular channel or barrel at a pressure of perhaps 2,000 pounds per square inch. A tuber having a 2½- or 3-inch screw

Figure 10.
Typical bead-wire let-off and gathering setup, utilizing Shook-type let-off stands.

has enough capacity for an FSW bead machine. A larger tuber can be used by reducing its speed or by employing a shallow-fluted feed screw in it. One man can operate a self-feeding tubing machine, the pull-off festooner, and a bead-winding machine. For such self-feeding, the rubber stock is taken from the mixing mill in long strips about 1½ inches wide, soapstoned or coated with zinc stearate, and coiled like a rope in large round cans or drums. Such expedients as placing a roller on the edge of the tubing-machine mouth to reduce friction on stock where it bends will help make the feeding more fully automatic.

The wire passes through the insulating head in a direction at right angles to the axis of the tuber screw. It is important that the wire be in correct alignment as it enters the die head. Because the tuber screw runs continuously, whether or not the wire is being pulled through the insulating head by the pull-off drums, an opening is provided for stock overflow. Rubber compound passing through the overflow is returned to the tuber and blended with fresh compound.

Frazier Type Head. Many tire manufacturers design and make their own insulating heads, and these naturally vary considerably in details, although they all produce about the same results. Typical of present-day insulating heads is the National-Standard Frazier Type, illustrated in Figures 19 and 20. The single or prefabricated wire from the let-off (reel stand) passes first through a baffle, which guides and spaces the wire and also prevents the rubber stock from traveling backward along the wire. The baffle opening is substantially the size and shape of the outside of the wire or wire assembly, and in the Frazier head it is so placed that it allows immediate removal of backflow to prevent freezing of wire in the baffle. Such freezing frequently occurs where a long passage is employed.

From the baffle, the wire passes through the rubber-stock cavity in the insulating head, where it becomes surrounded and coated with the rubber compound. In the case of braid or tape, pressure forces the rubber into all the interstices. Next the wire travels through the die, whose cavity is sized and shaped to control the distribution of rubber stock over it. In the Frazier head, the die is so constructed that it provides an adjustment whereby the opening can be closed as the die wears. The die actually serves to hold back all stock except that desired on the wire. The insulated wire next goes to the pull-off drum mounted on the festooner unit.

The baffles, or guide dies, and the insulating dies are changed according to the bead reinforcement to be handled. That is, one kind would be used for tape, another for braid, a third for a single strand, and still others for various numbers of strands forming a weftless bead reinforcement.

Figure 11.

Frazier insulating head for applying uncured rubber to bead wire.

The temperature of the rubber compound in the insulating-machine head is usually around 150°F. At the start, the head may have to be preheated; but after the insulator is in operation, pressure and friction in the rubber maintain the temperature. In fact, water-cooling of the extruder barrel is required in order to limit the temperature.

Pull-off. From the insulating head, the coated wire goes to the pull-off drums, which also serve as cooling units. Water circulating through the drums carries away heat absorbed from the insulating compound. At one time, these drums were only from 8 to 10 inches in diameter, which was satisfactory when 0.025-inch wire was being used to make bead-grommets 23 or 24 inches in diameter. But with the change to 0.037-

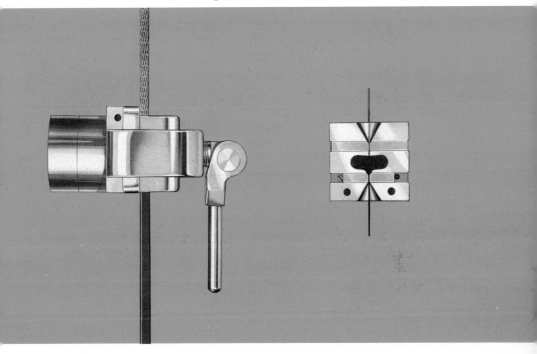

Figure 12.
Top view of Frazier insulating head, showing flat wire braid being covered with rubber compound.

Figure 13.
Vertical section of Frazier insulating head. Rubber insulation is being applied to wire braid or tape.

and 0.043-inch wire, and to bead-grommets only 15 or 16 inches in diameter, it was found that the small drums put too much cast or curve in the bead wire. And so pull-off drum diameters were increased to 18 and 20 inches.

Festooner. The bead wire, now partly cooled, next goes to the festooner. This is a machine which acts as a sort of storage unit to bridge the gap between the continuous operation of insulating the bead wire and the intermittent operation of winding the wire into bead-grommets. The festooner consists essentially of two sheave units, one composed of four sheaves and the other of five. Each sheave is grooved to accommodate the wire and is mounted to revolve independently. The upper, five-sheave unit is mounted in a fixed position at the top of the festooner tower, while the lower, four-sheave unit is mounted on a counterweighted block that can move up or down between the two parallel columns forming the tower. The wire is threaded around the upper and lower sheaves and finally is brought, from the upper unit, under a delivery sheave and a pawl which prevents it from moving backward when a completed bead is cut off.

When the bead-winding machine is taking wire faster than it is moving through the insulating head, the lower sheave unit of the festooner moves up the column, thus shortening the quantity of wire stored on the machine. If the unit moves upward far enough to operate a limit switch, the bead-winding machine stops. Also, as the lower sheaves move upward from the bottom position, another switch is tripped to start the pull-off drums. When the bead winder is not taking wire and the pull-off is operating, the lower sheaves of the festooner move downward, thus building up a backlog of stock (up to 135 feet) between the two sets of sheaves. At the bottom of its travel, the lower sheave unit operates a limit switch that stops the pull-off drums. Besides storing wire until needed, the festooner, by exposing a considerable length of insulated stock to the air, further promotes cooling of the insulation. Often additional cooling capacity is provided by a fountain unit, installed between the insulating head and the pull-off. This is a pan of water in which revolves a roller that applies water directly to the insulation. Riding on the fountain roller is a weighted rubber roller that removes surplus water. Sometimes an air jet is employed for such water removal.

After leaving the festooner, the bead wire goes to the bead-winding machine, where it is converted into bead-grommets.

The wire convolutions, because of the tackiness of the rubber insulation, generally adhere to each other sufficiently to enable the bead-grommet to be handled without difficulty. In some operations, ends of the wires are fastened with tabs of friction tape or with wire staples. When staples are used, they are applied by an automatic stapling machine immediately after the bead-grommet is removed from the winding machine.

Covering. If the bead-grommet is to be covered, it next goes to an operator, who runs it through a wrapping machine that applies either a spiral wrapping of square-woven rubberized tape or a strip of fabric whose edges are folded to make an overlapping seam, the strip thus becoming a sort of tube through which the bundle of wires extends.

Flipping. After being covered, the bead-grommet is ready for flipping. This is also a machine operation in which rollers and guides, in cooperation with manipulation by a skilled operator, fold one or more plies of rubberized fabric around the bead-grommet and extend the edges at the proper step-off to form a skirt. The skirt eventually ties the bead-grommet into the rest of the tire structure. Generally a strip of filler gum is placed around the outer circumference of the wrapped bead to fill the triangular cavity formed at the apex of the bead where the flipper fabric does not touch the bead-grommet. This is also called a bead-gum neck or apex strip.

The bead-making operation, from reel to wrapping, is an almost completely automatic process. One operator can take care of the insulator, pull-off and festooner, and bead machine.

Morris, or Yoder, Machine. Although the bead-grommet is, and generally always has been, built as a separate unit, to be combined eventu-

Figure 14.

**Morris, or Yoder, machine, which applied
fabric to parallel bead reinforcements, forming band
which was wrapped around core (left) to form
a tire casing.**

ally with the rest of the tire, the simultaneous building of bead and tire carcass has received much attention. In many of the early bicycle and motor-vehicle tires, the bead was formed as the fabric structure of the tire was assembled.

Machines have been designed and used for forming wire bead-grommets at the same time the tire is built. Typical of these is the Morris (after the inventor) machine, which also is known as the Yoder (after the manufacturer) unit. In 1917, when H. I. Morris was employed at the Savage Tire Company, in San Diego, California, he noticed the large accumulation of waste rubber and fabric trimmed from tires during manufacture. He began wondering whether there might be some way of building tires without so much waste. The result was the Morris machine and system for making tires and beads simultaneously.

The operation of the machine has been described by the inventor substantially as follows:

At the rear of the machine are mounted two reels of flat wire braid. The braid strips pass over a tension-control device and then over sheaves which guide them into grooves cut in the side edges of a steel plate called the "platen." Along each edge of the platen is also guided a strip of rubber-coated fabric. These strips are about 1½ inches wide, and the rubber coating, which is turned toward the braid, is of suitable compound to form a hard rubber when vulcanized. Slightly more than half the width of the strips extends over the edges, one being above and one being below the platen.

On the pedestal at the rear of the machine is mounted a roll of rubberized cord fabric and a liner take-up roll, together with a tension-control device over which the fabric travels. These rolls are set at an angle to the platen and, together with the tension control, are rotated around the platen, wrapping the cord fabric spirally on it. As the fabric is wrapped around the platen, it causes the rubber-coated fabric strips projecting beyond the platen edges to be folded about the wire braid. Thus the beads are enclosed in the side edges of a flat, tubular fabric band.

Four feed rolls at the front end of the platen pull the fabric forward as it is wrapped, the pulling speed being adjusted so the forward edge of each turn of fabric just meets the back edge of the preceding turn. The cord fabric is not bias-cut: but because it is wrapped at an angle, it forms a two-ply bias fabric strip, the upper ply crossing the lower one diagonally. The two plies are forced together as they pass over the feed rolls, completing a two-ply band of bias cords with the bead wires enclosed in each edge, ready to be formed into a tire carcass.

A collapsible core on which the tire is built is at the front of the machine. On each side of it is a detachable bead-forming ring, each ring having a clamp to engage the ends of the wire braid and hold them securely against the sides of the core. The bead clamps are not directly opposite each other but are positioned about 45 degrees apart.

Tension of the fabric band as it is wound on the core is controlled by the foot treadle near the floor at the front end of the base. The bead rolls (shown above the core) and the fabric rolls (shown behind the core) are controlled by air pressure. Tension on the band is registered on an indicator mounted directly in front of the forward pedestal.

The procedure of building a six-ply carcass is about as follows: With a hook knife, cords are cut through one ply only, just above the right-hand bead and parallel with it, for a distance equal to the width of the band. The triangular piece of one-ply fabric is stripped off, leaving both beads intact but with only one ply at the end of the band, forming a triangle between the bead wires, as shown in Figure 14. Ends of the bead wires are then clamped to the bead rings, with the leading edge of the band running across the core at an angle of about 45 degrees. The motor that drives the core is started, but because the drive is through a slipping friction clutch, the core does not move at this stage: the motor merely puts a tension on the band. The foot treadle is operated until the proper tension is registered on the indicator. A second motor is then started to drive the revolving roll support and feed rolls: this allows the fabric to feed to the core, and the core to revolve—tension on the fabric band remaining at the value set by the foot treadle.

The core is permitted to make three revolutions, which form a six-ply carcass. The bead wires are cut at points directly over the starting ends, and the cords are cut along the right-hand bead for a distance, measured from the bead end, equal to the band width. This permits a separation of the plies in triangular form, exactly matching the triangular section peeled off when the tire was started. The two single-ply triangular areas overlap exactly, making the tire carcass of uniform thickness.

The core is collapsed to permit removal of the tire carcass, after which the building operation is repeated for the next tire.

CHAPTER 8 § BICYCLE-TIRE BEADS

T HE EARLY pneumatic tires of Dunlop and others were made for use on bicycles and tricycles. Many of the pioneer bead developments described in preceding chapters were in connection with cycle tires, for the automobile tire did not become an important factor until almost the turn of the twentieth century.

For a time, particularly in the early 1900's, there was a veritable hodgepodge of tire types to bewilder the cyclist: solid rubber ones, cushion tires (solids with hollow centers) single-tube or "hose-pipe" tires, and double-tube varieties (casing with inner air tube) in clincher, wire-bead, and cemented-on-rim construction.

The New York Belting and Packing Company is said to have been the first American concern to manufacture bicycle tires, and its products probably included all types then known. At one period, every builder of bicycles was either a maker of his own peculiar kind of tire or had it manufactured by some other concern for exclusive use on his product. About the only company that seems to have made only tires—no bicycles or anything else—was Morgan and Wright.

In Great Britain, two-part tires having wire as a reinforcement in the beads of the shoe or casing appeared around 1890. The idea of a wire bead was contained in a patent issued to Charles Kingston Welch in England in 1890; and was patented, independently of Welch, by Alexander T. Brown and George F. Stillman in the United States in 1892. The soft-bead clincher tire appeared at about the same time. The William Erskine Bartlett patent of 1890 (British), covering the clincher idea, was acquired by the Dunlop Company about 1903. In the United States, Thomas B. Jeffery was granted patents on the clincher construction in 1891 and 1892. Also in this country, another nonwire tire, the

Figure 1. **Bicycle-type single-tube pneumatic tires were made by B. F. Goodrich in 1896 for this car built by Alexander Winton. It was said to have been the first American-made car sold in the United States, and the tires are considered the first American pneumatics made specifically for motor-car use.**

123

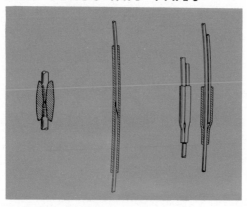

Figure 2.

Ferrules used on 0.072-inch bicycle-tire bead wire.

single-tube, was patented by Pardon W. Tillinghast in 1893. Thus the basic ideas adopted for pneumatic bicycle tires appeared in the course of 3 years or so.

Under several Jeffery patents, the earliest dated 1891, The B. F. Goodrich Company made clincher tires for the Gormully & Jeffery Company, builder of Rambler bicycles. These are considered the first clincher bicycle tires produced commercially in the United States. Men who were connected with the G & J tires recall that they were built and cured flat and upside down (wrong side out) on a drum whose surface was engraved with the tread design.

Dunlop, of England, is said to have licensed the Diamond Rubber Company, of Akron, Ohio, to make wire-bead tires as early as 1896, but there seems to be no indication that such manufacturing was done until 1904 or thereabouts.

Various Tire Types. Ultimately, bicycle-tire types began to be classified on a national or continental basis. The double-tube tire, protected by the patents of Welch and others, flourished in Great Britain. The single-tube type took root and grew luxuriously in the United States. In France, probably because of the influence of Dunlop interests, the double-tube tire became standard. English cyclists seem to have preferred the wire-bead type, while the clincher tire became popular in France.

The American single-tube tire might have nosed out the double-tube tire in Great Britain, France, and Germany if it had not been for the difficulty of making single-tube repairs. After this tire, which was the cheapest type to produce, had been on the market for some years, quick-repair methods and materials, including a puncture-sealing fluid that could be squirted into the tire, were developed. But in the meantime, the double-tube tire had gained too solid a foothold abroad to be dislodged. So, for a long time, the single-tube tire held a leading position in America, while the double-tube type was the favorite in Europe.

The influence of the early bicycle tires on motorcar tires was direct. In Great Britain, the first pneumatic automobile tire, said to have been made by Dunlop around 1893, was an inner-tube type having a casing equipped with wire-reinforced beads. The first pneumatic automobile tires recorded as being made in the United States, a set produced by The B. F. Goodrich Company for Alexander Winton in 1896, were enlarged copies of the single-tube bicycle tire.

Despite the popularity of the single-tube and clincher cycle tires, the wire-bead type has come out on top. Of course, a great many kinds of bead reinforcements have been tried, and some of them used in production; but round steel wire, in various sizes and arrangements, is reported to be the only successful reinforcement used in today's bicycle casings.

WIRE-BEAD TYPES

$\mathcal{T}$HE FOLLOWING are among the types of wire bead reinforcements that have been used in cycle tires:

Ferruled and Soldered. The original Welch tire beads consisted of a

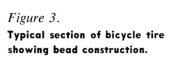

Figure 3.
Typical section of bicycle tire showing bead construction.

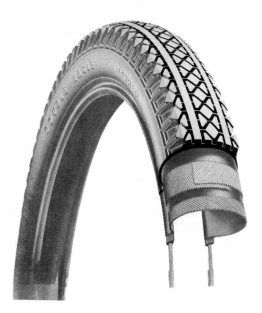

single turn of steel wire each. The ends were joined by a scarfed and brazed joint, and over this a steel sleeve was sweated. This type of joint continued in use at the Dunlop factory until 1935, when it was superseded by an electrically welded joint over which a sleeve was soldered. Beads of this type generally were made from 0.072-inch wire. It was, of course, important that the wire length be controlled closely so a bead-grommet with the required dimensions would be produced.

Several ways of using ferrules to reinforce joints in bicycle bead-grommets made of 0.072-inch wire have been developed. Three of these, shown in the accompanying drawings (see Figure 2), are typical.

1. Steel ferrule $\frac{7}{32}$ inch in diameter by 1 inch long, with one end necked down to about $\frac{9}{64}$ inch. Two ferrules are used on a bead, each fitting over one end of the wire at a lap joint. Ferrules are soldered in place.

2. A long, slender steel ferrule nearly $\frac{9}{64}$ inch in diameter (before installation) and $2\frac{1}{4}$ inches long. Ferrule is placed on wire forming the

Figure 4. **Hand-building cycle-tire covers, on formers in Dunlop factory, probably prior to 1925.**

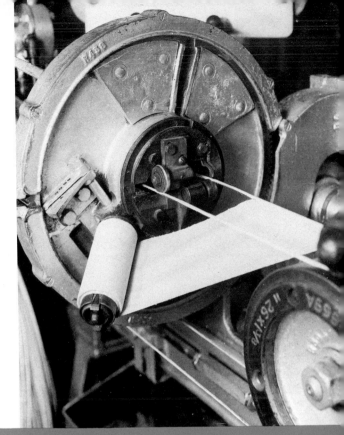

Figure 5.

Monoband machine for making cycle tires, introduced about 1927. Rubberized fabric was wound spirally around pair of wire bead-grommets.

Figure 6.

Power cutting machine for bicycle-bead wires. Introduced about 1928. Knife severs turns of wire wound on drum, forming wire rings.

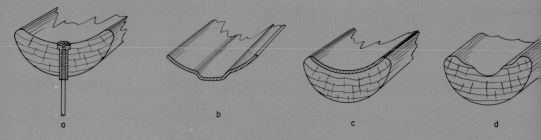

Figure 7. **Various forms of bicycle rims introduced prior to 1918. (A) crescent, wood, (B) crescent, steel, (C) crescent, steel-lined wood, (D) Dunlop, wood, (E) single-clinch, steel (F)**

bead-grommet, wire ends are beveled (skived), brought together in a butt joint, and brazed. Ferrule is moved over brazed joint, squeezed tight, and soldered.

3. A relatively short and thick steel ferrule having a grooved or threaded hole. Ends of wire are brought together in a butt joint inside this hole. Ferrule is squeezed to make threads bite into wire.

0.054-inch Wire. The bead-grommet was formed by winding large-diameter wire, usually 0.054 inch, around a mandrel for a number of turns, bringing the two ends together, and joining them with a metal ferrule secured with solder. Sometimes two ferrules, one over each end of the joint formed by twisting the wires together, were used. The wire was tinned to facilitate soldering, but rubber adhesion to the tinned surface was poor. This construction was tried by a number of manufacturers when the straight-side bicycle tire started its comeback, but turned out to be generally unsatisfactory.

A principal reason why the soldered and ferruled wire bead often left something to be desired is that a perfect soldering job was not done. It was the practice to use some sort of flux to ensure good adhesion of the solder to the wire and ferrule. Since the flux nearly always attacked the wire chemically, and the fabric surrounding the beads was not sufficiently water-resistant to keep moisture out, corrosion of the soldered joint resulted. Soldering the ferrule was a slow hand operation, and the workmen could not get the tubular bit of metal in the same position each time. As a result, the bead-grommet diameter varied. Because of the relatively few wraps of wire, any variation in the ferrule position was likely to be emphasized. As a result of imperfect soldering, corrosion, and differences in bead-grommet size, the soldered joints sometimes parted.

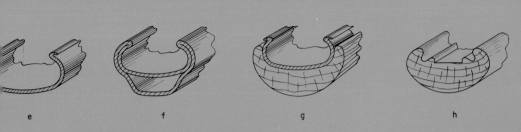

e f g h

single-clinch, hollow-steel, (G) single-clinch, wood-steel, (H) G & J double-clinch wood.

0.043-inch Wire. A construction used at The Goodyear Tire and Rubber Company for a short time consisted of a single 0.043-inch wire wound two turns around the bead-forming mandrel and overlapped 15 inches. In the 1930's, some companies were using two or three wraps of four 0.043-inch wires to make a bicycle bead-grommet.

0.025-inch Wire. The bead-grommet was made by running two or three wires of this diameter side by side through a tuber to coat them with rubber compound, then wrapping two or three turns around a former. Ends were overlapped 6 inches or so. This is essentially a small-scale application of the weftless bead reinforcement used in automobile tires. The 0.025-inch wire bead was discontinued because many manufacturers considered it too small and flimsy for easy handling.

0.037-inch Wire. One way of using 0.037-inch wire was to insulate it with rubber, wind the single strand around a former for the required number of turns (which varied according to the manufacturer's notions), cut for an overlap, and tape the ends.

A construction that finally was adopted by most bicycle-tire manufacturers and is being used today consists of running two 0.037-inch wires together through an insulating head to cover them with uncured rubber, wrapping them two turns around the bead former, overlapping the ends from 1 to 6 inches, and wrapping the splice with frictioned-fabric "spot stock" or tape. By thus using two parallel wires, bicycle bead-grommets can be made automatically on an FSW bead machine, which cannot handle a single wire.

Another method is to wind the two-wire rubber-covered tape over the fabric ply of the tire as it is positioned on the building drum—a process reminiscent of the early hand-building methods.

BICYCLE-TIRE MACHINES

*A*T FIRST, bicycle tires were hand-built by assembling the bead wires, rubberized fabric, and tread stock on a support of some kind. A typical setup, used by the Dunlop Rubber Company prior to introduction of the Healey-Shaw machine, consisted of a steel ring, or former, resembling the rim of a flat-belt pulley, mounted on collapsible spokes. The former face was wide enough to support a bicycle tire in the flat, or unformed, condition. Bias fabric was wrapped around the former, two bead-grommets slipped over it and positioned the proper distance apart, the fabric turned back over the wires, and more fabric and rubber applied until the tire was ready for shaping and curing. The collapsible spokes permitted the former to be reduced in diameter so the tire could be slipped off.

Healey-Shaw Bicycle-tire Machine. This machine employed a method of assembling bicycle-tire casings whereby the beads performed the functions of a drum. The two bead-grommets, welded or otherwise fastened at their joints to withstand the expansion force, were grasped by the machine and held in a position parallel to each other and separated a distance equal to the width of the tire, between beads, before it was shaped. The bead-grommets, when thus stretched, were in a form somewhat resembling ellipses, like a belt stretched between two pulleys. A band composed of cord-fabric plies was wound diagonally around straight portions of the two taut bead-grommets, the top and bottom fabric turns crossing each other at an angle. The fabric layers were forced into contact, the bead-grommets—after application of the tread—were moved toward each other as the tire was shaped, and finally the tire was cured in a mold.

The Monoband Machine. This bicycle-tire machine, similar to the Healey-Shaw, came into use at the Dunlop Company about 1927. It also was used for a time at The Goodyear Tire and Rubber Company, where, it is said, some difficulties were encountered because the bead wires had a tendency to creep during the operation. To reduce this action, the beads were semicured and sewed with fine thread applied in a loop stitch, with loops 1 inch or so apart.

Eccles Side-wire Machine. This machine applied strips of rubberized fabric to two wire bead-grommets simultaneously. The two bead cores, in a parallel position and the proper distance apart, were supported vertically on three grooved wheels. Guide rollers held the rings in the grooves. As the wheels and guide rollers, and therefore the bead-grommets, rotated, an outer and an inner band of rubberized fabric were applied circumferentially to the bead-grommets. The machine folded the fabric edges neatly around the bead cores, and the rollers and wheels "ironed" the two bands into contact.

Power Cutting Machine for Wires. This device, put into use about 1928 at the Dunlop Rubber Company factory, wound a single layer of bead wire on a drum and then converted the coil into rings by making a cut at right angles to the wire turns. This is similar to the way a jeweler makes chain links. The bead wires then were made endless by a brazed and ferruled or a welded joint.

BICYCLE RIMS

Out of the confusion of early bicycle tires and their corresponding rims, three general types appeared. In the United States, the single-tube tire (sometimes called the "hose-pipe tire" because it was built on a straight pipe mandrel like a rubber hose) was, for a long period, the predominant type. In Great Britain, the Dunlop wired-on tire, consisting of a cover (casing) and an inner tube, was preferred. In France and Germany, the clincher tire became popular. Reasons for the difference in preference in different countries, as already indicated, included the way patent litigation turned out; the fact that tire-puncturing hedge thorns were present on English bicycle paths; that wire-bead tires were easier to repair than single-tube ones (before the introduction in the United States of quick-repair tools and materials); and the fact that the single tube, in America, became cheaper to make than other types.

These various kinds of tires required different rims, and the bicycle-rim picture some years ago could be outlined as follows:

1. *Crescent-shaped Rim made of wood, metal, or wood with a metal liner.* Tires accommodated: Single-tube and the Morgan and Wright tire, which was a two-part type consisting of a tubular outer casing and a butt-end inner tube inserted through a laced slit 5 inches or so long in the rim side of the casing. Mounted on a crescent rim like a single-tube tire, the M & W could be removed and the tube taken out for repairing. Tires were held on crescent-shaped rims by cement.

2. *Clincher Rims.* There were two kinds, single and double clinch. The single-clinch rim was made (*a*) by rolling a single thickness of steel to shape, (*b*) by forming a tube into a clincher rim having a hollow center, and (*c*) by mounting a single-thickness steel channel on a wooden rim of crescent-shaped section. The double-clinch rim was shaped to accommodate the G & J bicycle tire. This rim usually was made of wood, and it accommodated only a double-clinch tire. Single-clinch rims, however, would accommodate either single- or double-clinch tires.

Some Early, Approximate Dates in Bicycle-tire and Rim Development

1816	Pedalless bicycle introduced. It was known by such names as "walking bicycle," "hobby horse," "dandy horse," and "Draisiene." Its origin has been attributed variously to French photographer Joseph Niepce and to an inventor named Drais.
1866	Appearance in France of the pedal cycle or "bone shaker."
1872	High-wheel "ordinary" bicycle with solid-rubber tires appeared in England.
1884	Cushion-type rubber tire introduced by Macintosh and Company in England. This was a hollow-center tire but was not pumped up.
1885	"Safety" bicycle with rear-wheel drive introduced. This was the forerunner of the modern bicycle.
1888	John Boyd Dunlop developed the pneumatic tire, but discovered after a time that Robert William Thomson had patented the pneumatic-tire idea in 1845.
1890	Charles Kingston Welch invented wire bead in Great Britain.
1889–1890	William E. Bartlett, said to have been an American, developed clincher-tire idea in Great Britain.
1891–1892	Thomas B. Jeffery patented clincher tire in the United States. First experimental tires of this type were made by The B. F. Goodrich Rubber Company in 1891. This tire became known as the "G & J."

132

1892–1893	Cord-fabric construction for tires patented in England and the United States by John F. Palmer and introduced by B. F. Goodrich for making single-tube cycle tires.
1893	Pardon W. Tillinghast patented single-tube or "hose-pipe" tire, which later became standard in the United States for a considerable number of years.
1895	Fred W. Morgan, of Chicago, invented a tire later marketed as the "Morgan and Wright." It was shaped like a hose-pipe tire but had a removable inner tube.
1896	Alexander Winton, of Cleveland, Ohio, placed an order with B. F. Goodrich for pneumatic tires for an experimental automobile he was building. These were made in the form of overgrown single-tube bicycle tires, those for the front wheels being 34 by 4 inches, and for rear wheels, 36 by 4 inches. These are said to have been the first pneumatic tires made in America expressly for automobile use.

Wire size has played an important part in the development of tire beads. Some of the major changes in bead construction were marked by a switch from one diameter of wire to another. More than once, a particular size of wire would be adopted by manufacturers as the standard for bead reinforcements, only to be dropped after a time because it proved to be too large and stiff, or too slender and unstable. For example, in making bicycle-tire beads, 0.025-inch wire looked for a while like the answer to all problems. But ultimately it was discarded in favor of a larger diameter because it was too limber, too difficult to handle.

Wire Manufacture. In the production of a particular diameter of wire, the starting point may be a steel rod or an intermediate size of wire. This is reduced in diameter by drawing it successively through dies of decreasing size. A die is made of something extremely hard, such as tungsten carbide or an industrial grade of diamond. Suitable lubricants are used to decrease friction between wire and die in order to lessen die wear and to improve the wire finish.

Diamond dies are used for small-diameter wires. The making of such a die is a process requiring a high degree of skill, care, and patience. The hole must be of precise shape and size, and the diamond must be as carefully polished as that in an engagement ring! Much of the work is done under microscopes.

Even though a wire die is made of one of the hardest substances known, the drawing of miles of wire through it will gradually wear and enlarge the opening. So a tungsten carbide die that originally produces, say, a wire 0.037 inch in diameter will, in time, be turning out wire that is slightly larger, such as 0.039 inch. If the manufacturing tolerance of such a wire size is plus 0.002 inch and minus 0.000 inch (which it is in

Figure 1.
Bead-wire drawing department in a modern wire plant.

Figure 2.
Modern facilities for finishing wire-drawing dies.

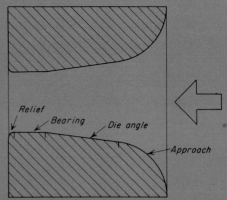

Figure 3.
Die used for reducing wire diameter in drawing operation. The "bull wheel" in photo draws wire through die. Sketch shows longitudinal section through a typical die.

this size), the hole in the die is made exactly 0.037 inch to start. Then, generally, many miles of wire can be drawn through it before it wears beyond the tolerance limit. When a die has worn too much for the wire size for which it was made, it is reworked to the dimensions of the next larger gauge. Thus a die starting out as a producer of very small wire progresses step by step until it eventually is turning out comparatively large wire. The largest size possible depends on the size of the diamond or the tungsten-carbide nib from which the die was made. Each passage of the wire through a die that reduces the wire diameter a little bit more is called a draft.

The act of drawing a wire has a hardening and stiffening effect on the steel, and because of this there are numerous manufacturing routines in which wire is heat-treated at some intermediate step or after the final draft. A low-carbon wire is said to be hard-drawn if it is pulled through all the intermediate sizes of dies to the final die without being annealed or otherwise heat-treated. In the case of high-carbon steel that is to be hard-drawn, as the starting point a rod or wire of intermediate size is given the desired properties by heat-treating. This is called patenting, which is a form of heat-treatment involving controlled heating and cooling. Fully annealed wire is heated to soften it after its final drawing and then is cooled slowly. Of course, all present bead wire is made of high-carbon steel.

Welding Bead Wire. When enough heat is applied to bead wire to produce a welded joint, the hardness characteristics of the steel are affected. One hazard is that the wire will be excessively brittle at the joint and therefore might break in service. The heat involved in brazing and hard-soldering wire can affect its hardness; and even soft soldering can exert some influence, especially if excessive heat is used. Automatic electric resistance welders join the ends of wire by raising the temperature to the fusion point; then apply a lower current, after the joint has cooled, to anneal the wire and thus eliminate brittleness. In one automatic welding system the welding is done while air is excluded from the wire; then the current is reduced and air is admitted to anneal the joint by slow cooling.

Carbon Content. Numerous kinds of wire have been used in tire beads, but often the selection has been made on the basis of carbon content. Low-carbon steel wire (maximum carbon about 0.25 per cent) was employed for various constructions of bicycle- and automobile-tire beads. Today, bead wire is in the high-carbon group (range of carbon content from 0.40 to 0.85 per cent). It is a hard-drawn wire whose processing must be carefully controlled through all the drawing, patenting, and other operations.

137

Wire size plays some part in determining the finish that can be applied (see Chapter 10). That is, some finishes are limited to wire within certain size limits.

Wire Gauges. Generally, in tire literature, the size of bead-wire diameter is stated in thousandths of an inch. However, various gauges or systems of stating wire diameters have been developed. Some of these pertain to steel wire, some to nonferrous wire. The table opposite lists the wire diameters for different gauge numbers in the more widely used systems.

Tolerances and Costs. When wire is made to a certain gauge diameter, the specifications customarily contain tolerances which give the manufacturer some leeway. Wire is usually sold by the pound and used by the foot in making bead-grommets. Because of this, there can be a variation in bead cost as a result of dimensional variations within tolerance limits.

Physical Properties. When calculating the strength of a bead reinforcement or of any other structure made of wire, when figuring the quantities of wire required for a certain application, or when determining other conditions involving wire, various physical properties of the wire must be known. In the table on pages 140 to 141, which lists steel wire by diameter in inches and in steel-wire gauge numbers, some of these properties are given.

Figure 4.

Patenting department for heat-treating steel rods which are to be drawn into bead wire.

GAUGE THICKNESSES

Name of Gauge		Steel Wire G. Washburn & Moen or W. & M. Wire G. U. S. Steel W. G.	Music Wire Gauge, M. W. G.	Brown & Sharpe Gauge, B. & S. G. A. W. G.	Stubs' Iron Wire Gauge, W. W. G. Birmingham or B. W. G.
Principal Use		Steel Wire, except Music Wire	Steel Music Wire	Non-ferrous Sheets and Wire	Flats, Steel Plates and Wire
Gauge Number	Millimeters Decimally	Thickness, Inch	Thickness, Inch	Thickness, Inch	Thickness, Inch
7/0's	12.45	.4900		.5800	
6/0's	11.72	.4615	.004	.5165	.500
5/0's	10.93	.4305	.005	.4600	.454
4/0's	10.00	.3938	.006		
3/0's	9.208	.3625	.007	.4096	.425
2/0's	8.407	.3310	.008	.3648	.380
0	7.785	.3065	.009	.3249	.340
1	7.188	.2830	.010	.2893	.300
2	6.668	.2625	.011	.2576	.284
3	6.190	.2437	.012	.2294	.259
4	5.723	.2253	.013	.2043	.238
5	5.258	.2070*	.014	.1819	.220
6	4.877	.1920*	.016	.1620	.203
7	4.496	.1770*	.018	.1443	.180
8	4.115	.1620*	.020	.1285	.165
9	3.767	.1483*	.022	.1144	.148
10	3.429	.1350*	.024	.1019	.134
11	3.061	.1205*	.026	.0907	.120
12	2.680	.1055*	.029	.0808	.109
13	2.324	.0915*	.031	.0720	.095
14	2.032	.0800*	.033	.0641	.083
15	1.829	.0720*	.035	.0571	.072
16	1.588	.0625*	.037	.0508	.065
17	1.372	.0540*	.039	.0453	.058
18	1.207	.0475*	.041	.0403	.049
19	1.041	.0410*	.043	.0359	.042
20	.8839	.0348	.045	.0320	.035
21	.8052	.0317	.047	.0285	.032
22	.7264	.0286	.049	.0253	.028
23	.6553	.0258	.051	.0226	.025
24	.5842	.0230	.055	.0201	.022
25	.5182	.0204	.059	.0179	.020
26	.4597	.0181	.063	.0159	.018
27	.4394	.0173	.067	.0142	.016
28	.4115	.0162	.071	.0126	.014
29	.3810	.0150	.075	.0113	.013
30	.3556	.0140	.080	.0100	.012
31	.3353	.0132	.085	.0089	.010
32	.3251	.0128	.090	.0080	.009
33	.2997	.0118	.095	.0071	.008
34	.2642	.0104	.100	.0063	.007
35	.2413	.0095	.106	.0056	.005
36	.2286	.0090	.112	.0050	.004
37	.2159	.0085	.118	.0045	
38	.2032	.0080	.124	.0040	
39	.1905	.0075	.130	.0035	
40	.1778	.0070	.138	.0031	
41	.1676	.0066	.146	.0028	
42	.1575	.0062	.154	.0025	
43	.1524	.0060	.162	.0022	
44	.1473	.0058	.170	.0020	
45	.1397	.0055		.00176	
46	.1321	.0052		.00157	
47	.1270	.0050			
48	.1219	.0048			
49	.1168	.0046			
50	.1118	.0044			
	.1016	.004			
	.09144	.0036			
	.08128	.0032			
	.07112	.0028			
	.06096	.0024			
	.05080	.0020			
	.04064	.0016			
	.03556	.0014			
	.03048	.0012			
	.02540	.0010			

Steel Wire Ga. No. W. & M.	Diameter in Inches	Area in Square Inches	Breaking Strain 100,000 Lbs. Per Sq. In.	Weight, Pounds Per 1,000 Ft.	Feet Per Pound
	.0010	.00000079	.079	.00267	374924
	.0012	.00000113	.113	.00384	260364
	.0014	.00000154	.154	.00523	191288
	.0016	.00000201	.201	.00683	146455
	.0018	.00000254	.254	.00864	115716
	.0020	.00000314	.314	.01067	93731
	.0022	.00000380	.380	.01291	77464
	.0024	.00000452	.452	.01536	65091
	.0026	.00000531	.531	.01803	55464
	.0028	.00000616	.616	.02091	47822
	.0030	.00000707	.707	.02405	41660
	.0032	.00000804	.804	.02731	36614
	.0034	.00000908	.908	.03084	32404
	.0036	.00001018	1.018	.03457	28929
	.0038	.00001134	1.134	.03851	25967
	.0040	.00001257	1.257	.04268	23433
	.0042	.00001385	1.385	.04704	21250
50	.0044	.00001521	1.52	.05164	19366
49	.0046	.00001662	1.66	.05644	17718
48	.0048	.00001810	1.81	.06145	16273
47	.0050	.00001964	1.96	.06668	14997
46	.0052	.00002124	2.12	.07212	13866
45	.0055	.0000238	2.38	.0807	12394
44	.0058	.0000264	2.64	.0897	11145
43	.0060	.0000283	2.83	.0960	10415
42	.0062	.0000302	3.02	.1025	9753
	.0065	.0000332	3.32	.1127	8824
41	.0066	.0000342	3.42	.1162	8607
40	.0070	.0000385	3.85	.1307	7652
39	.0075	.0000442	4.42	.1500	6665
38	.0080	.0000503	5.03	.1707	5858
37	.0085	.0000567	5.67	.1927	5189
36	.0090	.0000636	6.36	.2160	4629
35	.0095	.0000709	7.09	.2407	4154
	.0100	.0000785	7.85	.2667	3749
34	.0104	.0000849	8.49	.2885	3466
	.0105	.0000866	8.66	.2940	3400
	.0110	.0000950	9.5	.3228	3098
	.0115	.0001040	10.4	.3525	2835
33	.0118	.0001094	10.9	.3714	2693
	.0120	.0001131	11.3	.3841	2604
	.0125	.0001228	12.3	.4168	2400
32	.0128	.0001287	12.9	.4370	2288
	.0130	.0001327	13.3	.4508	2218
31	.0132	.0001369	13.7	.4647	2152
	.0135	.0001433	14.3	.4861	2057
30	.0140	.0001539	15.4	.5228	1913
	.0145	.0001651	16.5	.5607	1783
29	.0150	.0001767	17.7	.6001	1666
	.0155	.0001889	18.9	.6415	1559
	.016	.0002011	20.1	.6828	1465
28	.0162	.0002061	20.6	.7000	1429
	.0165	.0002140	21.4	.7267	1376
	.0170	.0002270	22.7	.7709	1297
27	.0173	.0002351	23.5	.7983	1253
	.0175	.000241	24.1	.8167	1224
	.0180	.000255	25.5	.8642	1157
26	.0181	.000257	25.7	.8738	1144
	.0185	.000269	26.9	.9135	1095
	.0190	.000284	28.4	.9645	1037
	.0195	.000299	29.9	1.014	986.2
	.0200	.000314	31.4	1.067	937.3
25	.0204	.000327	32.7	1.110	900.9
	.0205	.000330	33.0	1.121	892.1
	.0210	.000346	34.6	1.176	850.0
	.0215	.000363	36.3	1.233	811.0
	.0220	.000380	38.0	1.291	774.6

Steel Wire Ga. No. W. & M.	Diameter in Inches	Area in Square Inches
	.0225	.000
24	.0230	.000
	.0235	.000
	.0240	.000
	.0245	.000
	.0250	.000
23	.0258	.000
	.0260	.000
	.0270	.000
	.0280	.000
22	.0286	.000
	.0290	.000
	.0300	.0002
	.0310	.0002
21	.0317	.0002
	.0320	.0008
	.033	.0008
	.034	.0009
20	.0348	.0009
	.035	.000
	.036	.0010
	.037	.0010
	.038	.0011
	.039	.0011
	.040	.0012
19	.041	.0013
	.042	.0013
	.043	.0014
	.044	.0015
	.045	.0015
	.046	.0016
	.047	.0017
18	.0475	.0017
	.048	.0018
	.049	.0018
	.050	.0019
	.051	.0020
	.052	.0021
	.053	.0022
17	.054	.0022
	.055	.0023
	.056	.0024
	.057	.0025
	.058	.0026
	.059	.0027
	.060	.0028
	.061	.0029
	.062	.0030
16	.0625	.0030
	.063	.0031
	.064	.0032
	.065	.0033
	.066	.0034
	.067	.0035
	.068	.0036
	.069	.0037
	.070	.0038
	.071	.0039
15	.072	.0040
	.073	.0041
	.074	.0043
	.075	.0044
	.076	.0045
	.077	.0046
	.078	.0047
	.079	.0049
14	.080	.0050

OF STEEL WIRE

...aking Strain ...00 Lbs. ...Sq. In.	Weight, Pounds Per 1,000 Ft.	Feet Per Pound
39.7	1.348	741.8
41.5	1.411	708.7
43.3	1.470	680.3
45.2	1.536	650.9
47.1	1.601	624.9
49.1	1.667	599.9
52.3	1.775	563.3
53.1	1.8032	554.5
57.3	1.9444	514.3
61.6	2.091	478.2
54.2	2.182	458.4
66.1	2.245	445.4
70.7	2.400	416.6
75.5	2.564	390.0
78.9	2.680	373.1
80.4	2.731	366.1
85.5	2.906	344.3
90.8	3.084	324.3
95.1	3.23	309.6
96.2	3.27	306.1
01.8	3.46	289.3
07.5	3.65	274.0
13.4	3.85	259.7
19.5	4.06	246.3
25.7	4.27	234.3
32.0	4.48	223.0
38.5	4.71	212.5
45.2	4.93	202.8
52.1	5.16	193.7
59.0	5.40	185.2
66.2	5.64	177.2
73.5	5.89	169.8
77.2	6.02	166.2
81.0	6.15	162.7
88.6	6.40	156.2
96.6	6.67	149.8
04.3	6.94	144.1
12.4	7.21	138.7
20.6	7.49	133.5
29.0	7.78	128.6
37.6	8.07	123.9
46.3	8.36	119.6
55.2	8.67	115.3
64.2	8.97	111.5
73.4	9.28	107.8
82.7	9.60	104.2
92.3	9.93	100.7
01.9	10.25	97.53
06.8	10.42	95.98
11.7	10.59	94.4
21.7	10.92	91.53
31.8	11.27	88.74
42.1	11.62	86.07
52.6	11.97	83.54
63.2	12.33	81.10
73.9	12.70	78.74
84.8	13.07	76.52
95.9	13.44	74.40
07.2	13.83	72.32
18.5	14.21	70.37
30.1	14.61	68.45
41.8	15.00	66.65
53.7	15.41	64.89
65.7	15.82	63.21
77.8	16.23	61.61
90.2	16.65	60.06
502.7	17.07	58.58

Steel Wire Ga. No. W. & M.	Diameter in Inches	Area in Square Inches	Breaking Strain 100,000 Lbs. Per Sq. In.	Weight, Pounds Per 1,000 Ft.	Feet Per Pound
	.081	.005153	515.3	17.50	57.14
	.082	.005281	528.1	17.93	55.77
	.083	.005411	541.1	18.37	54.42
	.084	.005542	554.2	18.82	53.13
	.085	.005672	567.2	19.27	51.89
	.086	.005809	580.9	19.73	50.68
	.087	.005945	594.5	20.19	49.53
	.088	.006082	608.2	20.65	48.43
	.089	.006221	622.1	21.13	47.33
	.090	.006362	636.2	21.60	46.29
	.091	.006504	650.4	22.09	45.27
13	.0915	.006575	657.5	22.33	44.78
	.092	.006648	664.8	22.58	44.30
	.093	.006793	679.3	23.07	43.36
	.094	.006940	694.0	23.57	42.43
	.095	.007088	708.8	24.07	41.54
	.096	.007238	723.8	24.58	40.68
	.097	.007390	739.0	25.10	39.84
	.098	.007543	754.3	25.62	39.03
	.099	.007700	770.0	26.15	38.24
	.100	.007854	785.4	26.67	37.49
	.101	.008012	801.2	27.21	36.75
	.102	.008171	817.1	27.75	36.04
	.103	.008332	833.2	28.30	35.34
	.104	.008495	849.5	28.85	34.66
	.105	.008659	865.9	29.41	34.00
12	.1055	.008742	874.2	29.69	33.69
	.106	.008825	882.5	29.97	33.37
	.107	.008992	899.2	30.54	32.74
	.108	.009161	916.1	31.11	32.14
	.109	.009331	933.1	31.69	31.56
	.110	.009503	950.3	32.27	30.99
	.111	.009677	967.7	32.86	30.43
	.112	.009852	985.2	33.46	29.89
	.113	.010029	1002.9	34.06	29.36
	.114	.010207	1020.7	34.66	28.85
	.115	.010387	1038.7	35.27	28.35
	.116	.010568	1056.8	35.89	27.86
	.117	.010751	1075.1	36.51	27.39
	.118	.010936	1093.6	37.14	26.93
	.119	.011122	1112.2	37.77	26.48
	.120	.011310	1131.0	38.41	26.04
11	.1205	.011404	1140.4	38.73	25.82
	.121	.011499	1149.9	39.05	25.61
	.122	.011690	1169.0	39.70	25.19
	.123	.011882	1188.2	40.35	24.78
	.124	.012076	1207.6	41.01	24.38
	.125	.012272	1227.2	41.68	24.00
	.126	.012469	1246.9	42.34	23.62
	.127	.012668	1266.8	43.02	23.25
	.128	.012868	1286.8	43.70	22.88
	.129	.013070	1307.0	44.39	22.53
	.130	.013272	1327.2	45.08	22.18
	.131	.013478	1347.8	45.77	21.85
	.132	.013685	1368.5	46.47	21.52
	.133	.013893	1389.3	47.18	21.20
	.134	.014103	1410.3	47.89	20.88
10	.135	.014314	1431.4	48.61	20.57
9	.1483	.017273	1727.3	58.66	17.05
8	.162	.020612	2061.2	70.00	14.29
7	.177	.024606	2460.6	83.56	11.97
6	.192	.028953	2895.3	98.32	10.17
5	.207	.033654	3365.4	114.3	8.75
4	.2253	.039867	3986.7	135.4	7.39
3	.2437	.046645	4664.5	158.4	6.31
2	.2625	.054119	5411.9	183.8	5.44
1	.283	.062902	6290.2	213.6	4.68

T HE FINISH of wire has had an important bearing on tire-bead development. Sometimes, in reviewing the difficulties manufacturers encountered in earlier years of bicycle- and automobile-tire making, it is evident that either too little attention was given to the wire finish or too little was known about it.

For example, tinned wire was used for soldered and ferruled bead-grommets many years ago. The tinned surface made soldering easier. It also was thought that the tin coating did a lot to retard corrosion of wire in a bead during use. The belief later was proved to be mostly wishful thinking. Then, too, there may have been some who thought that the tin plating improved rubber adhesion, whereas the chemical adhesion between tin and rubber is practically nil. Because of the poor adhesion, and in spite of the tin plating, rusting of tinned-wire bead-grommets (which usually were of 0.054-inch gauge) was common.

Cold-drawn steel wire may be given either a drawn finish or a coated finish. The first type is applied during or before the final passage of the wire through the drawing die. The second type (coated finish) is applied after the final drawing operation.

Some finishes used now or in the past on bead wire are as follows:

Bright. The common bright finish, sometimes called lime bright, is a dull gray produced by coating the wire with lime or a substitute material just before the final drawing operation. *Extra-bright* wire has a higher degree of brightness achieved by careful attention to pickling, drawing, etc. Rubber adhesion to bright wire is poor.

Liquor Finish (abbreviated "L.F."). Before being drawn to final size, the wire is placed in an acid solution of tin and copper salts. By chemical displacement, a coating of tin and copper is formed on the wire. After plating, the wire is drawn, either with or without lubricants, depending on the brightness and other characteristics desired. For an extra liquor finish, the wire is given tin-copper coatings between more than two successive drafts. The color of liquor-finish wire ranges from straw to silvery white, depending on the proportions of the two coating metals. There are size limits to wire that can be drawn with a liquor finish. Rubber adhesion to L.F. wire is fair.

Coppered. This finish is produced in a manner similar to liquor finish, except that only copper is used as the coating. Wire having a coppered finish has been used in bicycle beads where welded or brazed bead-grommets were required. Adhesion of this finish to rubber is considered erratic, because of the difficulty of maintaining the proper coating of copper.

Bronze Plate (abbreviated "B.P."). By chemical displacement, the wire is given a coating of bronze (copper-tin alloy). The coating is nearly all copper, the tin being present in very small percentage.

Brass Plate. The wire is electroplated to produce the coating of brass (copper-zinc alloy).

Rubber adhesion to bronze and to brass is good. These finishes are not, in themselves, highly resistant to corrosion.

Galvanized. The wire surface is coated with metallic zinc in one of two ways: (1) The wire is run through a bath of molten zinc. As it emerges, it may pass through wipers. The wiping step results in a thinner coating than when the wire is permitted to retain all the zinc that adheres to it. (2) The wire is run through an electroplating bath, where zinc is deposited on it from a solution of zinc salts. Wire can be drawn after it has been galvanized. Zinc provides good protection against corrosion. Rubber adhesion to it is poor.

Tinned. The wire is coated with tin by being run through a bath of the molten metal, or through an electroplating tank where the tin is deposited from a solution of tin salts. Rubber adhesion to tinned wire is poor, and corrosion resistance is not high.

AP-1 Finish ("Avery Process No. 1"). The wire is first given a coating of zinc for corrosion resistance; then copper is electroplated over it for rubber adhesion. The AP-1 finish is sponsored by the National-Standard Company. The story of its development reflects some of the problems that have confronted the makers of tires and bead reinforcements.

Prior to 1926, flat wire braid had become the chief reinforcement in straight-side tires, almost to the exclusion of every other form of wire. The wire used in making braid had either a liquor or a tin-plate finish, neither of which had good corrosion resistance. However, almost no trouble was experienced with rusting of braided wire. This was primarily due to the nature of the braid, which allowed better coverage of bead stock and permitted an interlocking action of the many interstices to give a mechanical adhesion that was not easily broken.

In 1926, Pierce tape, a less yielding material than braid, was brought to the tire industry. (In that year the National-Standard Company became the exclusive licensee under the Pierce patents and sponsored Pierce tape to the industry. R. C. Pierce was with The B. F. Goodrich Company when the tape that bears his name was invented.) The use of this tape for beads made it necessary to control bead diameters more closely than when braid had been employed, in order to reduce possibilities of fatigue in the bead. Sometimes the Pierce-tape bead-grommet would develop movement relative to the surrounding rubber compound, and there would be a separation of wire and rubber. Because of this loosening, and aided perhaps by a pumping action, moisture would penetrate to the wire, causing it to rust. At first, Pierce tape was made of tinned wire. Later, bronze-plated wire was used for better adhesion, but corrosion continued to be too common.

Between 1926 and 1935, this corroding of bead wire became so serious that the National-Standard Company set out to find methods of coating wire so that good corrosion-resistance plus good rubber-adhesion characteristics would be possible without reducing the physical characteristics of the metal. The company sponsored a fellowship at Mellon Institute to be devoted exclusively to this problem; and it arranged for Dr. Colin G. Fink, of Columbia University, who was considered at that time to be the outstanding electrochemist in the country, to work with National-Standard technicians. Many wire coatings were tried, but most of them proved too expensive for practical purposes.

Figure 1.
Plating bead wire.

In 1932, the searchers for a better wire coating came into contact with Edward L. Avery, who had developed a process for putting a copper coating over galvanized wire. His method, while itself not adapted to commercial use, formed the nucleus for a process that was practical. Avery had other processes in mind, so the zinc-copper coating method developed from his ideas was named "Avery Process No. 1."

Color Changes in AP-1 Finish. When the wire is first processed, it has a uniform, rich copper color. If it is kept in storage for a time or comes into contact with moisture, there is a migration of the copper into the zinc, causing the coating to take on a whitish color or become the hue of light brass. This is called "white flash." The change in color and the migration that caused it do not materially affect the corrosion resistance of the wire or its rubber-adhesion characteristics with most rubber compounds.

Although it was developed in connection with the use of Pierce tape, the AP-1 finish is equally useful on all other types of wire bead reinforcement.

EFFECT OF FINISH ON RUBBER ADHESION

*I*N A TIRE BEAD, the adhesion between rubber and wire not only affects bead strength and stability during and after manufacture, but it also influences the corrosion resistance of the wire. The rubber compound can be considered as both a paint and an adhesive. As a "paint" it prevents moisture and other corrosive agents from reaching the wire. As an "adhesive" it is important, for on it depends the degree of adhesion obtained with the wire finish. For example, variations in carbon-black content of rubber cause corresponding variations in adhesive properties of the compound.

Chemical Adhesion. As already indicated, different metals applied as finishes to steel wire have different effects on the adhesion between the wire and a rubber compound. They also have different degrees of corrosion resistance. Rubber adheres best to copper and its alloys, brass and bronze. It does not adhere well to bare steel wire or to tinned or zinc-coated wire. Rubber adhesion to wire having an AP-1 finish is about the same as to that having a B.P. finish. Any variation between the two is often traceable to differences in the rubber compound.

Mechanical Adhesion. The nature of adhesion between rubber and wire also may be mechanical. Even with a tinned or zinc-coated wire, where chemical adhesion is virtually zero, there may be some mechanical adhesion between the wire and a coating of rubber. Otherwise, it would require no effort at all to pull the wire out of its rubber jacket. This adhesion might be regarded as a form of friction. But practically, such adhesion often can be considered as nonexistent, so far as contributing to the union between bead-grommet and bead rubber is concerned. However, if the wire strands forming the bead-grommet are arranged or shaped so the rubber can get a mechanical grip on the bead-grommet as a whole or on any element of it, mechanical adhesion may be considerable. This condition is best exemplified by flat wire braid. The hundreds of interstices formed in a bead-grommet by the interweaving of the wire strands making up the braid permit an interlocking of rubber and wire. That is, the rubber compound, during the vulcanizing stage, softens and flows into the interstices and around the wires; then it hardens and forms a secure mechanical union.

In present-day beads which employ single-wire or weftless bead-grommet construction, the adhesion between rubber and wire is almost wholly of the chemical variety. Mechanical adhesion can be considered negligible. In beads using Pierce tape, mechanical adhesion is better: in those using braid, it is greatest. When mechanical adhesion is good, a wire finish having high chemical adhesion to rubber is not so essential as when mechanical adhesion is poor. Thus a flat wire braid having a liquor finish is practical because of the high mechanical adhesion with rubber. There is fair chemical adhesion too—liquor finish being better in this respect than, say, tinned wire. For maximum adhesion, a braid having a bronze-plate or AP-1 finish is specified.

Judging Adhesion. During the early period when adhesion to rubber was first being considered as an important factor in evaluating bead wire, all tests were made by visual inspection of the bead wire pulled from a pad of rubber in which it had been vulcanized. If rubber remained on the wire, adhesion was considered to be good. It soon was discovered that this method, in itself, was not the complete answer, and so the "pounds-pull" method was developed—a test procedure wherein the force required to separate the wire from the rubber pad is an important factor.

If, after the wire is pulled from the test pad, there is rubber adhering to it, the bond strength is greater than the rubber strength. So if better adhesion is required, the compound must be altered to improve its strength. By such alteration, it is possible for the strength of the rubber to exceed the bond strength; and when this point is reached, the wire will pull out bare, but at a higher pounds pull than with the unaltered compound. The higher pounds pull indicates better adhesion; and rubber coverage of the wire is used to judge whether the finish or the compound must be altered to improve adhesion. Even though these two methods—

Figure 2.

Test sample showing mechanical adhesion of rubber bead stock to braided wires.

Figure 3.

Preparing a test pad for determining rubber adhesion to bead wire.

147

visual inspection and measurement of pounds pull—are used together to evaluate adhesion, some inexplainable discrepancies often occur. Since adhesion is due to a chemical reaction at rubber-metal interface, both materials are important factors in obtaining optimum results.

Typical Adhesion Performance. A study was made of rubber adhesion to 0.037-inch wire. Five test pads of rubber were prepared, each containing one wire with tinned finish, one with bronze-plate finish, and two with AP-1 finish. The rubber stock was cured for 1 hour at 260°F. Pads, after being vulcanized, were stored for 20 months before adhesion tests were made. The results were as shown below. The pull required to loosen wire (third column) at no time can exceed the stress required to shear the rubber.

Pad No.	Wire Finish	Pull Required to Loosen Wire, Lb.	Adhesion by Visual Inspection, Per Cent
1	Tinned	225	20
	B.P.	228	75
	AP-1	250	100
	AP-1	242	100
2	Tinned	205	5
	B.P.	228	50
	AP-1	249	100
	AP-1	254	100
3	Tinned	183	10
	B.P.	265	60
	AP-1	273	100
	AP-1	263	100
4	Tinned	206	5
	B.P.	215	50
	AP-1	268	90
	AP-1	260	100
5	Tinned	165	5
	B.P.	212	50
	AP-1	268	100
	AP-1	270	100

EFFECT OF WIRE FINISH ON CORROSION RESISTANCE

$\mathcal{T}$HE RESISTANCE to rusting of wire in a tire bead depends on the wire finish and on the degree of adhesion between it and the surrounding rubber compound. In former years, the rubber structure of a bead could admit considerable water. Today, better compounds make this a less likely occurrence.

During the period when 0.054-inch wire was being used widely for bead-grommets, tin was considered an essential finish. It was thought to be corrosion-resistant, but later it was found that tin gives no practical protection against rusting. It does facilitate soldering in the making of a twisted or ferruled joint. Tin as a bead-wire finish was discontinued about 1930.

A bronze-plate finish on wire provides no appreciable protection against rusting, but it does improve rubber adhesion. As a result, a wire with a B.P. finish, having good rubber adhesion, is more resistant to corrosion than a tinned wire, having better corrosion resistance but no adhesion. This is because the rubber adhering to a wire can be considered as a protective finish, much like paint. If the adhesion is good, the rubber prevents moisture from reaching the metal; if it is poor, movement of the bead while the tire is in use can cause separation and permit or even assist moisture to enter. The result is a rusty bead-grommet. In a salt-spray test, tinned wire without a rubber covering resists corrosion for 4 hours, while bronze plate resists it only ¾ hour.

Zinc as a wire coating (either hot-dipped or electroplated) gives excellent protection against corrosion, but rubber will not adhere to it.

Steel bead wire having an AP-1 finish proved to be the answer to many bead-corrosion problems with which tire companies were wrestling in the 1930's. Also, the process solved a vexing problem involving wire for export. Much rusting of wire on reels had been occurring in export shipments, particularly those crossing the equator. Variations in temperature caused moisture to condense on the wire, and rusting followed. The first AP-1 wire ever made commercially was shipped from Michigan to the Yokohama Rubber Company, in Japan, in 1932. This wire was made on the first experimental processing unit, before a production unit had been put into service. The wire made the trip without corroding, thereby solving a problem that had been causing considerable concern among engineers at the factory in Japan.

Even though wire having an AP-1 finish may be somewhat more costly than B.P. wire having equivalent adhesion characteristics, bead specialists consider the greater corrosion resistance of the AP-1 wire to be worth the difference in cost. They believe that there is always present the possibility that moisture will work into a bead and cause corrosion of wire that is not fully protected. Many a veteran tire engineer can remember more than one occasion when, in the days of liquor-finish and B.P. wire beads and more permeable rubber, he cut apart a bead and found the bead-grommet almost completely disintegrated into rust.

Synthetic Resin. During the manufacture of a bead, it is important that the uncured rubber compound adhere to the wire bead-grommet sufficiently well to permit handling and to prevent undue movement of the wire before vulcanization is completed. In order to increase adhesion to

1	PHYSICAL PROPERTIES	Physical properties covered by sections B, C, D, and E are to be determined by Scottgraph.
A	Gauges	0.054 in. average, 0.053 in. minimum, 0.055 in. maximum.
B	Breaking loads	630 lb per wire minimum, regardless of gauge.
C	Ultimate tensile strength	Average—285,000 psi; maximum—300,000 psi; minimum—265,000 psi.
D	Elastic limit	65 to 95 per cent of ultimate tensile strength.
E	Elongation at break	2.5 per cent minimum in 10 in.
F	Bending	Wire must withstand a sharp right-angle bend with pliers and then be straightened to original position without splitting. Plier jaw edges to be rounded to 0.027 in. radius. Test to be repeated minimum of four times at different sections of wire.
G	"Bone" or rigidity	(Instructions were given for running a bone test on the wire. See Chapter 13 for a description of such a test.)

uncured rubber compound, a synthetic resin that is similar to the natural resins in crude rubber is applied to the bead wire by spraying or by wiping with saturated pads. After its job of holding the uncured compound more securely is finished, the resin migrates into the rubber during vulcanization.

Other benefits result from the use of the resin. When applied to wire that has a copper finish (B.P., AP-1), it reduces discoloration of the copper by sulfur fumes, encountered during shipment and storage. The resin, being a moisture-resistant coating, helps to prevent other types of corrosion, as from condensation. But the most important benefit is that it increases the adhesion between wire and uncured rubber. It has no effect on the adhesion of cured rubber.

Wire Specifications. Tire manufacturers had no comprehensive specifications for bead wire, other than those pertaining to tensile strength, until about 1920. Wire manufacturers had worked out detailed specifications before that date and used them to maintain control over their manufacturing processes.

A tire manufacturer's records of 1931 for 0.054-inch bead wire (now obsolete) included the points tabulated here.

2	TINNING	The wire shall be double tinned.
3	COIL SIZE	Wire shall be furnished in coils of approximately 80 lb each. Wire shall be unwound counterclockwise, the starting end of each coil to be indicated by a tag.
4	WRAPPING	Each coil shall be wrapped in waterproof paper, and wire ends tied down to prevent their breaking through wrapper.
5	TAGGING	Each coil shall be tagged to show breaking load and gauge. Also, in every carload, 12 coils shall be tagged to show gauge, breaking load, twist, elastic ratio, bone, and elongation at break.

Oil on Wire. In a wire mill, certain types of wire (such as rope wire) are treated with oil. This is to assist in keeping the wire from rusting while in storage and also to assist in the manufacture of the rope, etc. Bead wire should not have an oily surface at any time; but if, by any chance, oil should get on the wire, it must be removed before the wire comes into contact with rubber. Various industrial degreasing methods can be used.

CHAPTER 11 § BEAD-WIRE ENEMIES

ire Fatigue. The condition known as wire fatigue can be described as the gradual degeneration leading finally to failure (as by breaking) and results from repeated stresses which at no time are as great as a single stress that would cause the same sort of failure.

Conditions which localize the fatigue-producing stresses can hasten failure of the bead reinforcement. As an example, the welded-cable bead-grommet, used around 1918, gave trouble because stresses, which were distributed uniformly throughout most of the ring, tended to concentrate in the vicinity of the welded joint, where the wire had been subjected to welding heat that altered its tensile characteristics. In other words, the cables would break at or near the weld.

Repeated stresses may cause first a work-hardening of the steel. This can be demonstrated by bending an annealed wire (such as a paper clip that has been heated red hot and cooled slowly) back and forth in the same place. The bend (stressed region) exhibits an increased stiffness after a number of flexings. Now continue the bending, and you will feel the wire suddenly weaken; and in another bend or two it will break. Thus the application of repeated stresses has, first, caused the wire to become harder and stiffer; then, second, continuation (or a sudden increase in the magnitude) of the bending has caused fatigue failure by breaking.

Examine the surface of a fractured piece with a microscope, and you will find that it looks like a break in a very brittle, crystalline material. It is just that—steel wire whose crystalline structure, originally modified by heat-treatments to give it great strength, toughness, and flexibility, has been rearranged by fatiguing forces.

Stresses on Wire in a Tire Bead. In its job of holding a tire on a rim, the wire bead-grommet has to resist a constant pull exerted by the tire-inflation pressure. Therefore the wire is under a uniform stress. In addition, when the wheel is turning there are superimposed various other tensions resulting from varying centrifugal force, road bumps, braking, effects of the travel wave developed in the tire, corner turning, and so on. Since these superimposed stresses vary, the bead wire is subjected to fatigue. Probably such fatigue is involved in nearly all present-day bead-wire failures which—compared with those of some years back—are rare occurrences.

Early "Rim Jumpers." Before the introduction of the straight-side tire, the tensile strength of beads was not an important factor in tire design. In a clincher tire, the hook, or clinch, provided the necessary restraining force to hold the tire on the rim. But when the straight-side tire appeared, this job was taken over by the bead reinforcement. Because knowledge of tensile requirements was not extensive at the start, there was a period, quite disturbing to tire men, during which "rim-jumping" tires—a not uncommon type among clinchers—continued to plague the straight-side type. And the straight-side, with its inextensible beads, had been introduced partly to eliminate just such troubles as rim jumping!

Flat wire braid was being used successfully by Goodyear as a bead reinforcement and provided one way of reducing rim jumping. But for a long period the patented braid was not available to other manufacturers. So the reduction of jumping, through general improvement of tensile and other properties of bead-grommets by means of such devices as piano-wire and stranded-wire constructions, had to wait until the slow process of experience, experiment, and development provided the know-how. In 1911, production of flat wire braid for tire beads was started by the National-Standard Company.

There is another important factor usually involved in bead-wire failure in service. This is corrosion. It is believed that virtually all cases of service failure of wire bead reinforcements are caused jointly by corrosion and fatigue. More will be said about corrosion later in this chapter.

Early Rubber Compounds. When the straight-side tire came into general use, more attention had to be given to the rubber compound used in the beads. In the clincher tire, about all the compound had to do was fill space and be able to stretch over rim flanges. It generally was made of the least costly materials, including just enough new or reclaimed rubber to produce a semihard, stretchable mass. But in the straight-side bead, it was found that the rubber had a much more important job to do. It had to be compounded to provide good adhesion to wire the instant it was applied, and before and after curing; to provide good adhesion to surrounding materials; and to be flexible, but not elastic or brittle. Even now, poor adhesion during the process of applying insulation to bead wire may cause pores in the rubber coating. These can trap air and moisture, which causes blows during curing or results in eventual rusting of the wire.

CORROSION AND VIBRATION IN TIRE BEADS

$\mathcal{V}$ARIOUS VIBRATIONS which give rise to the fatigue-producing stresses superimposed on a wire bead-grommet may be traceable to or influenced by a number of conditions.

Poor Adhesion. When adhesion between the bead wire and surrounding rubber is poor, the wire may move or vibrate independently, resulting in a separation between the metal and rubber. This frequently admits moisture and other corroding agents, so that the wire becomes subjected to corrosion as well as to fatiguing stresses. When adhesion is good, wire and rubber tend to behave as a unit, vibration in the wire is dampened, and moisture and other corrosive materials are kept out.

Conversely, corrosion which breaks down the bond between rubber and wire can encourage vibration. Thus chemical action between ingredients of the rubber compound and the wire or wire finish might cause corrosion which could be followed by less resistance to vibratory forces.

A phenomenon developing from lack of adhesion is the "singing bead," sometimes called the "squealing" or "musical" bead. Vibration of the bead reinforcement is within the audible range, and the ear hears the "music," "squealing," or whatever the sound.

Manufacturers who changed from flat wire braid to tape, single-wire, or weftless construction have encountered adhesion troubles because they lost the very high mechanical adhesion associated with braid. Before the new bead reinforcements could be successful, satisfactory surface adhesion had to be established.

Tire-Rim Relations. Damaging stresses can be imposed on the tire beads by conditions involving the wheel rim. A tire that fits tightly on its rim is less subject to both corrosion and vibration in the bead regions than a loose one.

The early straight-side tires were made with beads whose diameters generally were about $\frac{1}{16}$ inch greater than the diameters of the bead seats on the flat-base rims; some manufacturers maintained a smaller

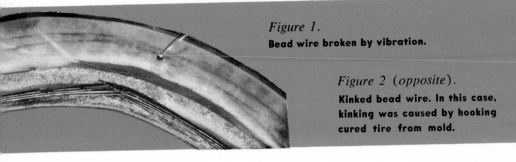

Figure 1.
Bead wire broken by vibration.

Figure 2 (opposite).
Kinked bead wire. In this case, kinking was caused by hooking cured tire from mold.

difference, around $\frac{1}{32}$ inch. Because of this clearance, the tires were subject to creeping and the effects of the "travel wave." Such a wave results from the action of the tire tread in rolling along a roadway. The tread rubber tends to bunch up at the point where it first makes contact with the road: much like the piling up of water ahead of the prow of a boat. The resulting displacement of particles travels as a wave continuously around the tire; and the stresses act to pull the bead away from the rim where wave meets bead—at a spot that progresses in step around the bead. Such travel waves act as fatiguing stresses on beads which fit loosely on the rim. The waves can cause crystallization in bead wire, manifested as hardness or brittleness that may cause breaking if the beads are subjected to severe shock.

The drop-center rim has sloping bead seats, which allow a snug fit. Therefore the beads are tightly wedged on the rim and are less subject to vibration.

The tight-fitting bead also seals out water, whereas the older, loose-fitting beads on straight-side rims permitted moisture to get beneath them. Present-day truck tires have beads that fit tightly on sloping seats; yet they can encounter trouble from rim rusting caused by water that enters around the valve-stem hole. When such rusting progresses far enough to cause the bead to loosen on the rim, vibration can begin to get in its punches. The remedy, in the case of truck tires, is mostly constant inspection and cleaning and painting of the rims. Bead seats that are integral with detachable flanges or locking rings can be replaced when badly corroded.

The tubeless automobile tire, because a tight, uniform fit between bead and rim is essential and because of sealants that may be used around the beads, is normally immune to vibration and corrosion traceable to bead looseness.

Kinked Bead. If the wire bead-grommet has been kinked by improper handling during manufacture or at any other time, the kinked spot, even

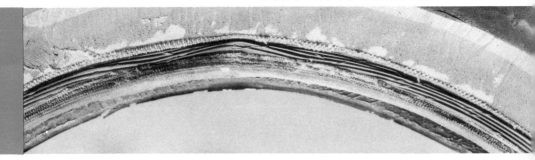

though straightened, is a potential locale for trouble. Vibratory forces traveling around the bead-grommet tend to concentrate at the kink, and crystallization and eventual failure at that point may result.

Corrosion of Wire in a Bead. Bead corrosion in the tire used to be a serious problem. Today, thanks to better wire coatings and improved rubber, it is one of the lesser matters in the tire maker's trouble book. However, no bead can be considered free from the threat of corrosion, for the reason that it may not remain watertight. Damage to rubber and fabric, through careless handling and installation of the tire or as the result of accident, normal wear, and deterioration of the rubber with time, can permit oxygen, water, and various other chemical substances to reach the wire. When this happens, corrosion is likely to follow.

Kenyon Tests. It has been customary to evaluate bead wire on the basis of separate corrosion and fatigue tests. In the 1930's, a series of studies [1] was carried out by John N. Kenyon, of Columbia University, with a pulsating torsion-fatigue machine, for the purpose of evaluating the protection given by various metal platings. These tests indicated that bead-wire performance can best be predicted on the basis of corrosion tests carried on while the sample is being subjected to variable stresses.

The Kenyon testing machine consisted essentially of a tank for holding oil or water, a pair of inclined bearings in which the ends of the 15-inch wire test sample could rotate, a motor for rotating the wire in the bearings, and accessory equipment. During the test, the wire was curved downward through the liquid by the guiding action of the inclined bearings. A typical test consisted of rotating the wire, usually at 6,000 revolutions per minute, in distilled water of a certain pH (regulated acidity) value,

[1] John N. Kenyon, "A Corrosion-Fatigue Test to Determine the Protective Qualities of Metallic Plating and a Pulsating Tension-Fatigue Machine for Small Diameter Wire," *Proceedings of The American Society for Testing Materials,* Vol. 40, pp. 705–770, 1940.

in a weak solution of sodium chloride, or in some other liquid; counting the number of revolutions before failure of the specimen by breakage; and then examining the condition of the wire after the run.

While these tests may not have been considered by some to be conclusive, they indicated the following:

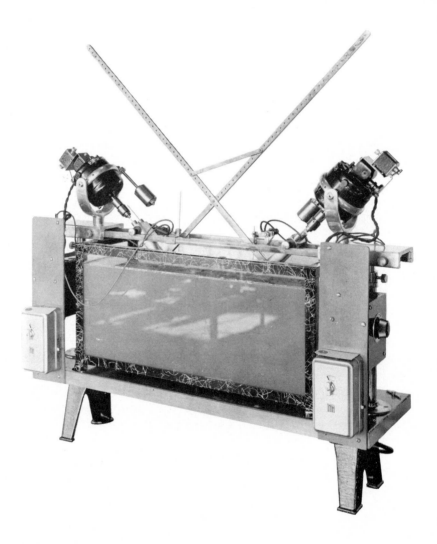

Figure 3.

Machine used in making corrosion-fatigue tests on bead wire.

Wire hot-dipped in zinc and then plated with copper (AP-1 finish) shows high fatigue resistance because of its high resistance to corrosion.

Bronze-plated wire and unplated steel wire soon become brittle from combined corrosion and stressing.

Bronze-plated wire may become brittle more quickly than unplated wire because the copper-steel combination permits electrolytic action at every break in the plating. The steel acts as the anode (positive pole) and thus is etched away. When the wire has been plated with zinc, similar action is supposed to take place, but this time the zinc is the anode, and the steel (cathode) is not corroded.

Wire coated with zinc and then with copper remained ductile enough after a test to be wound into a slender coil spring. Unplated and bronze-plated wires were so brittle after a comparable test that they broke abruptly when bent.

Other Causes of Corrosion. Some of the causes of corrosion of bead wire in a tire have been mentioned, such as lack of adhesion between wire and rubber; movement of the thereby loosened wire, which causes suction that "pumps" water into beads; and beads that fit loosely on the rim. There are some other causes.

Rubber is not absolutely impermeable to water. It can absorb moisture. In former years it was much worse in this respect than in this day of improved compounds. The fabric incorporated in a tire bead is made of cotton or other textile material, and if water reaches this through the surrounding protective rubber, the fabric begins to act like a lampwick and conducts the water toward the bead wire. The fabric may be exposed to moisture through a break or a worn spot; or the bead may be kept so wet that moisture works its way through the rubber until it wets the fabric. Such a "drowned bead" condition, where the bead is subjected to water for long periods, may be especially expected when the bead does not fit the rim tightly enough.

When water does reach the bead reinforcement, along with oxygen and perhaps other chemical substances, it may be assisted in its attack upon the wire by the presence of chemicals in the rubber compound. Thus water, oxygen, and free sulfur can unite to form sulfuric acid (H_2SO_4); and a weak solution of this acid can dissolve an 0.037-inch bead wire in a few days.

Although the bead-wire corrosion common in the old days—when beads were loose-fitting on the rim and the resulting movement sucked in water, when rubber compounds were likely to permit capillary action, and so on—is supposed to be a matter of history, there are tire men who feel that today's bead rubber sometimes is not so perfect as it might be. Often, they say, a bead compound is changed without too much thought being given to its effect on adhesion with the bead wire. Also, they intimate that the stock used for making beads has, upon occasion, been known to be primarily an accumulation of odds and ends of rubber compounds, rather than a carefully planned composition. For maximum freedom from bead-wire corrosion and fatigue, the rubber compound should be carefully engineered to fit conditions.

BEADS IN STORAGE AND SHIPMENT

*A*LL BEAD wire is subject to tarnishing and corrosion under adverse storage and shipping conditions.

Naturally, wire having a corrosion-resisting finish is less subject to rusting at any time. Thus a wire with an AP-1 finish does not corrode so readily as bronze-plated wire. However, no finish can be considered wholly corrosionproof, and the wire must be handled accordingly.

When wire is prepared for shipment, the reels are always covered with a water-resisting material, which in the past has been a waterproof paper and V.P.I. (vapor phase inhibitor). After it leaves the factory, such a reel may be subjected to conditions that would cause this or any other protection to fail.

Condensation. Conditions which neutralize protective measures usually are such that moisture condenses on the wire surface, perhaps even wetting the wire throughout the coil. This alone, plus atmospheric oxygen that is always present, is enough to cause eventual corrosion; but it may be helped by the presence of chemicals, in the form of atmospheric fumes, dust, and vapors.

Any sudden change in temperature in the presence of moisture-laden air may cause condensation on wire in storage or transit. At night, the wire becomes cool. Later, warmer, moisture-laden air striking it will transfer some of its moisture burden to the cool metal. It has been found that in California, bead wire cannot be left overnight in a boxcar without becoming wet from condensed moisture.

In more than one tire plant having troubles with rusty bead wire, it has been discovered that the wire reels were stored near leaking steam pipes. The wire, normally cooler than the escaping steam, soon would become waterlogged as a result of condensation. Likewise, men looking for causes of rusting have found reels of wire stored beneath leaking water pipes, under leaky roofs, and in similar unsuitable places; and left too long on docks, or unprotected from snow and rain.

The story is told about a wire-company representative who was called on the carpet by a tire manufacturer because rusty beads had been found in the finished tires.

The wire salesman listened patiently to the complaints, then asked, "May I see your wire-storage room?" He was conducted to a neatly kept warehouse chamber containing orderly rows of bead-wire reels. Windows were tight. There was no evidence of leaks of any sort. He could smell no chemical odors. He examined the wire on several reels. None showed any signs of corrosion.

"And you take the wire directly from this room to the bead machines?" the wire man asked.

"Not exactly," a tire-company man said. "Here, I'll show you." He led the way to a building that housed a power plant. As he opened the door, they were greeted by the blast from a safety valve on a steam boiler. He pointed to a dozen or so reels of wire in double file along one side of the boiler room. "We found," the tire man continued, "that if we leave the wire here for a little while, its surface roughens up just a bit. Makes it better for rubber adhesion, you know."

The wire salesman said nothing: he was speechless. But later he did a lot of talking, trying to explain the connection between the initial corroding of the wire and the rusting that was destroying the finished beads.

Preventing Corrosion. To prevent corrosion damage to wire before it reaches the tire, the following recommendations should be kept in mind:

Store wire where rain, snow, leaking water, escaping steam, and corrosive chemicals cannot reach it.

Store it where there will be no sudden temperature changes.

Avoid prolonged storage. One manufacturer was discovered who had some reels of wire that were over 4 years old. They had been put into the warehouse first and had remained undisturbed because the warehouseman found it easier to move the ones nearer the loading platform. The wire on those back-row reels was a total loss. During a strike, another factory owner had poured oil over his stored reels of wire in an effort to prevent corrosion; but the protective paper had prevented the oil from reaching the wire, which rusted anyway. To avoid too-long storage, the wire user should rotate his stock on a first-in, first-out basis.

BEADS WORKING

A "WORKING" bead in a tire is one whose bead-grommet separates from the surrounding rubber and fabric because of poor adhesion between metal and rubber. The "singing beads" already mentioned are an example of beads working. The old 0.054-inch piano-wire bead would squeak because of looseness or lack of insulation. The wire in a bead may squeak because of poor adhesion of the insulating material. Braid and Pierce-tape bead reinforcements never have been known to squeak or sing, because of the additional mechanical adhesion these types of wire impart to the bead.

The working of bead-grommets made of a single wire wound around and around to form a cable sometimes caused the entire length of wire to come out of the bead as the tire was in motion.

A bead-grommet may work because it is too large and therefore does not hold the tire tightly enough on the rim. Oversized bead-grommets can get into a tire as a result of mistakes or carelessness during manufacture.

HEAT IN BEADS

*A*BSORPTION OF energy by a material causes its temperature to rise. In a tire bead-grommet, stresses, imposed by various conditions, can generate heat. A bead-grommet that has been separated from the surrounding rubber and fabric will, as a result of movement, generate sufficient heat in a short time to char the fabric and cause the rubber to become soft and tacky. With continued operation, the fabric and rubber will slough away and actually expose the bead-grommet before complete failure of the tire.

Brake Heat. A major source of heat which affects beads is the nearby brake. The energy transformed into heat at the brake drum is tremendous in the case of a heavy truck, bus, or airplane. Because of the rapid deceleration of considerable mass from a high speed to zero speed, an airplane-wheel brake drum may become a cherry red from the heat developed in it. Such generation of heat in a brake assembly is of interest to the tire manufacturer because of the proximity of the beads. Higher passenger-car speeds have given rise to the suggestion that the drop-center rim may be replaced by a flat-base type so that larger-diameter brake drums can be used. This would, of course, bring the heat still closer to the tire bead and might involve some bead-design problems.

Heat in sufficient quantity may cause softening of the rubber in the bead structure, as already noted in connection with truck tires. This can affect the adhesion between rubber and metal, and perhaps cause the bead-grommet to loosen throughout. Subsequently, troubles arising from loose beads may be experienced. Proper tire design requires that the bead structure have a sufficient resistance to the effects of any heat to which it is likely to be subjected.

Multiple Beads. The placing of greater demands on the beads of tires, as a result of ever-increasing speeds and loads, was the primary reason why a construction involving more than one grommet per bead was introduced around 1916. The first dual beads are believed to have been made by the Armstrong Rubber Company, in Garfield, New Jersey. They came into use in truck and heavy-duty tires. Some companies used the Pratt cable bead in multiple. Beads with three, four, and five grommets have been made for extremely heavy tires. Advantages of multiple beads include the following:

Because of wider distribution and separation of masses of wire and rubber, heat build-up is less centralized.

Rocking of beads on the rim is reduced, thus enabling the tire to withstand heavier, more continuous loading.

Figure 4.
Multiple beads, such as the dual type shown, were developed in an effort to lick the heat problem in tires.

A stronger union exists between bead-grommets and surrounding plies of fabric.

Stress in bead structure is distributed more uniformly.

The bead reinforcement can approach more nearly the ideal of getting the wires against the rim base. In some designs, flipper strips have been omitted, the cord plies of the tire carcass being brought around the bead-grommets in the form of turnups. Thus there might be no more than, say, three plies between bead and rim.

Greater strength can be built into the beads, thus increasing the safety factor.

On the disadvantage side, the complexity and therefore the cost of manufacturing multiple beads are considerably greater than for single beads.

CHAPTER 12 § OTHER SOURCES OF

BEAD TROUBLE

*B*ead Sizes. A bead, being a carefully engineered part of a tire, must be of the right size in order for it to function harmoniously with other components.

Beads of improper diameter can result from mix-up of bead-grommet sizes during manufacture. For example, the bead-grommet for a six-ply tire is slightly larger than that for a four-ply tire, because of the different thicknesses of fabric and rubber between wire and rim. If a four-ply tire bead-grommet is built into a six-ply tire, the bead will be too small; if a six-ply tire bead-grommet is used in a four-ply tire, the bead will be too large.

A bead-grommet that is too small may break during the curing stage of manufacture. However, it is more likely that it will not break, but will compress the fabric and rubber beneath it to such an extent that these materials will be displaced, the bead toe becoming thinned and extended.

Bead-grommet Too Large. When an oversized bead-grommet is built into a bead, forces applied during manufacturing operations may cause it to become wavy or kinked. There may be separation between turns of the wire. Kinking often causes a corresponding distortion of nearby fabric and rubber. Thus a kink arched toward the sidewall may cause a thinning of the bead at that point, because fabric and rubber move into the space, under the bead-grommet, that should have been occupied by the wire.

If a tire having an oversized bead-grommet is put into service, the various stresses that travel around the bead tend to concentrate wherever there is a kink. Fatigue becomes more pronounced at that point and may result eventually in the breaking of the bead-grommet. Or the oversized bead may become loosened from its surrounding rubber and fabric.

165

Besides mix-ups in bead-grommet sizes during manufacture, over-sized or undersized beads can result from inaccurate or careless engineering calculations.

Once a bead-grommet made of weftless or single-strand wire or Pierce tape is formed and the wire ends properly secured, the diameter and circumference cannot change appreciably, either during or after manufacturing operations. A bead-grommet made of flat wire braid, which has some "give," can adjust itself to some extent before the rubber insulation has been hardened by vulcanization. But after being cured, its size is fixed—a result of the locking, or riveting, action of the hard rubber compound which fills the interstices among wires.

Reclaiming Beads. Sometimes tire makers are asked why they do not remove the wire bead-grommets from old tires and use them again. In a modern, well-designed tire, the bead will outwear the tread and carcass in nearly all cases. If the wire bead-grommet is cut out, it will be found to be, in appearance at least, as good as when new. Physical properties of the wire may have been altered some by the action of fatigue-producing stresses, but there still are plenty of miles left in the average scrap-tire bead-grommet.

The chief reason why tire bead-grommets cannot be re-used is that size requirements are too important. Each one must be sized precisely for the tire in which it is to be used, so that it will be neither too small nor too large. A slight change in tire design requiring different ply thick-

Figure 1. **Bead construction in which bead-grommet diameter is (a) normal, (b) oversized, and (c) undersized.**

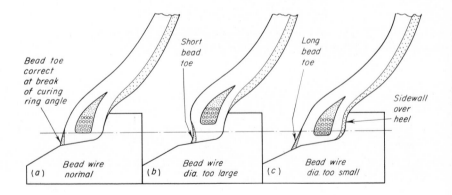

ness under the bead-grommet will make necessary a corresponding change in the circumference of the bead-grommet. Perhaps this will amount to only a few thousandths of an inch. To select from a quantity of reclaimed bead-grommets those which would meet such limited size requirements would be a difficult and costly operation. So every new tire comes out of the factory with brand-new wire in its beads.

Bead Stack. The term "stack" refers to the cross-sectional structure of the bead-grommet. When a wire reinforcement such as a flat wire braid is wound several turns around a former, the braid layers are piled, or stacked, one on top of the other.

Bead troubles have been caused by the wrong kind of bead stack. Engineers recommend that in the case of single beads (a bead where only one stack of wire is employed) the stack should be made as nearly square as possible, to avoid undue distortion of the wire arrangement. In today's method of manufacture where only one stack of wire is used, the surrounding fabric must turn around the stack, and in so doing it may disarrange the wire if the stack is not properly proportioned and held together. In the case of dual beads where undercut shoulder drums are used during the tire-building stage, the beads remain more nearly in the position in which they are applied, because the material does not turn around the wire stack but merely adjusts itself under curing inflation tension.

ABUSE IN MANUFACTURE

*B*EAD TROUBLES, when they do occur, often can be traced to error or abuse during manufacturing operations. Some of the errors which result in tires being classified as "seconds" are caused by such things as mix-ups in bead-grommet size (such as getting a four-ply tire bead in a six-ply tire) and inaccurate calculations in connection with bead designing.

Another source of trouble is the use of old equipment. Modern machines for processing beads and tires have eliminated many of the inaccuracies and other shortcomings associated with older equipment; but a lot of the old equipment still remains in use.

Storage of Uncured Tires. Kinks in bead-grommets, which lead ultimately to failure in service, are often traceable to improper handling or storage of the tire before it has been cured. Once a bead has been kinked, there is no feasible way of straightening it; so if it is cured into a tire, the kink is cured in, too.

Kinked beads are caused, before curing, by: (1) Letting the uncured tire lie on a flat surface. Weight of the fabric and rubber will cause it to flatten, thus kinking each bead at two diametrically opposite points. (2) Hanging the uncured tire on a slender peg or other similar support. This causes a single severe kink in each bead-grommet. (3) Folding the tire so the bead is kinked. (4) Piling something on the tire.

To avoid kinking beads during storage, hang the uncured tire on a saddle whose top surface is curved to match the curve of the beads and which is large enough to support the beads for, say, 25 per cent of their circumference. The uncured tire should not be folded at any time in such a way that the wire is kinked, and tires should not be piled or otherwise subjected to weight that might cause distortion or kinking of the beads.

Curing Bags. Stiff rubber tubes inflated with air or water are inserted inside tires during curing, to hold them in shape and exert pressure that forces them into contact with the mold. Tire beads can be damaged during removal of the curing bags, or during removal of the tire from the mold.

Mold surfaces are lubricated to prevent tires from sticking too tightly. Usually, press equipment is made to impart a slip motion to the mold as it opens, which breaks the tire loose from the base rings. However, a tire occasionally will stick to one of the mold halves and must be forcibly removed. The moving force is applied through hooks inserted around

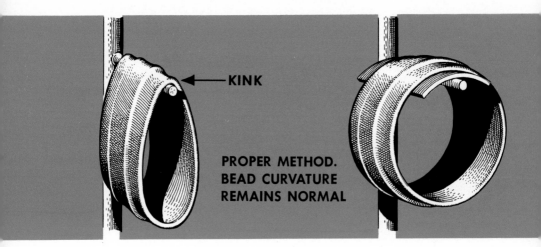

KINK

PROPER METHOD.
BEAD CURVATURE
REMAINS NORMAL

one of the beads. Unless a great amount of care is used, a hook is likely to put a permanent kink in the bead wires. Using a broad hook helps, but even then there is danger of damaging the beads.

Debagging a cured tire is done by pulling the bag out with a power-operated hook. This pulling action involves considerable force which, if allowed to act improperly upon a wire bead-grommet, can cause serious kinking of the wire. Beads should be supported by hydraulic hooks or other arrangement so the curing bag can be drawn over them without causing damage.

Curing-bag Contours. The water and air bags can be causes of bead troubles in other ways. A mix-up of bag sizes in the factory can result in either too much or too little compression of the bead area during the curing operation. Bags change their contours with use and should be checked periodically to make certain that such change has not made them unfit for further use.

When a new bead design is developed, the contours of the curing bags should be changed to match the new design.

A curing bag that exerts too much pressure can distort the wire in a bead.

Turnups and Tie-ins. These fabric plies, which form part of the bead structure, must be properly engineered and followed through for every new tire design. A change in their number or arrangement without corresponding change of the wire bead-grommet can alter the compression on a bead so much that the bead-grommet is, in effect, too large or too small.

Figure 2.
Bead wire in this uncured tire is kinked by being hung on a peg. Proper method of supporting tire is on a saddle whose curvature matches that of the beads.

PLACING TIRE ON FLAT SURFACE OR PEG IS POOR PRACTICE

Figure 3.
An uncured, unformed tire with beads kinked by lying on a flat surface.

KINK

ABUSE IN MOUNTING

*A*FTER A bead has gone through the various manufacturing operations and has been incorporated into a finished tire without being subjected to kinking or other distortion, it still has some hazards to face. Such hazards result from carelessness or ignorance of persons attempting to apply the tire to, or remove it from, a rim.

The drop-center rim used on all passenger cars and most small trucks has, at the center, a well, whose diameter (not width) at the bottom is less than that of the tire beads. The two beads are supposed to be pressed together at one point so they will move all the way to the bottom of the rim well, thus permitting them to pass easily over the rim flanges in a sort of buttonholing operation.

All too frequently, a service-station attendant or other person inexperienced or careless in the art of installing and removing tires will use a heavy mallet or crowbar, or both, to force over the rim flanges a bead that has not been positioned properly in the rim well. In fact, at least one service attendant was found who was of the belief that modern straight-side tire beads are supposed to stretch like the old, soft clincher type!

The use of any prying or hammering force may cause the wire in a

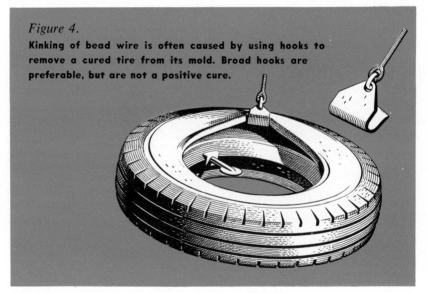

Figure 4.

Kinking of bead wire is often caused by using hooks to remove a cured tire from its mold. Broad hooks are preferable, but are not a positive cure.

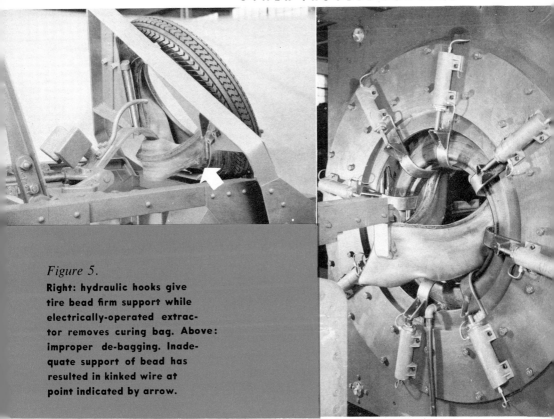

Figure 5.

Right: hydraulic hooks give tire bead firm support while electrically-operated extractor removes curing bag. Above: improper de-bagging. Inadequate support of bead has resulted in kinked wire at point indicated by arrow.

bead to be kinked or to separate from the surrounding rubber and fabric. This sets the stage for later failure, particularly if the damage has been severe.

Bead Lubrication During Installation. Tire manufacturers and installers recommend simple precautions, to be taken during installation of tires on drop-center rims, that will eliminate possible bead damage and subsequent tire failure. To avoid bead jamming or improper seating during tire inflation, the technicians advise that the beads of a tire always be lubricated just before installation. The lubricant permits the beads to slip more easily into proper position, thus avoiding any sudden surge that might damage them.

Soap solution is used as a lubricant. A suitable solution is prepared by diluting Murphy's Oil Soap with water to a consistency that permits easy application with a brush. The soap is applied to the outside of each bead and for 1 or 2 inches inside the casing. The portion of the inner tube that will be adjacent to rim and beads is soaped also: this will help it to seat without being pinched or creased. Water introduced by such soaping into the bead and rim areas soon is dissipated and creates no rusting hazard.

There is little justification for lack of knowledge of how to apply and remove a modern pneumatic tire. Most tire manufacturers have published information on the subject. The Rubber Manufacturers Asso-

Figure 6. **Proper method of applying tire on drop-center rim, and**

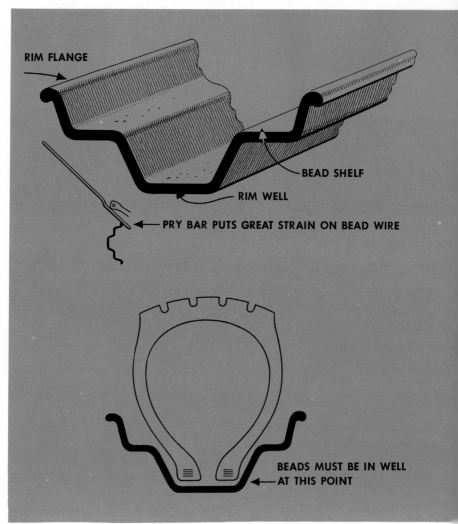

RIM FLANGE

BEAD SHELF

RIM WELL

PRY BAR PUTS GREAT STRAIN ON BEAD WIRE

BEADS MUST BE IN WELL AT THIS POINT

ciation, 444 Madison Avenue, New York 22, New York, has issued booklets describing proper methods of mounting and demounting tires on drop-center rims. An example is "How to Get Extra Service out of Automobile Tires." Methods of removing and applying tires with the wheel on a mounting rack and with the wheel on the floor are described.

Reading and understanding such manuals will make tire-mounting and demounting operations easier and will make it possible to avoid many bead injuries which ultimately may result in tire failure.

danger points where bead can be damaged during the operation.

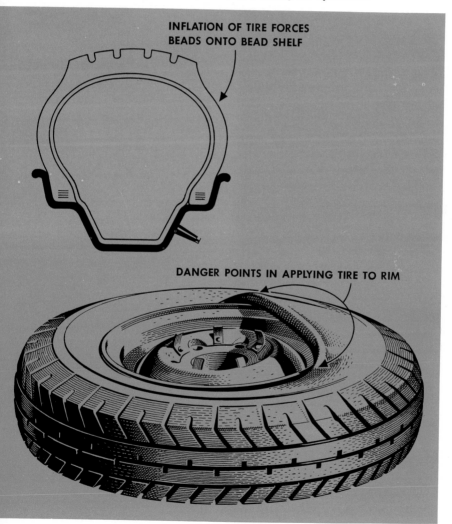

INFLATION OF TIRE FORCES
BEADS ONTO BEAD SHELF

DANGER POINTS IN APPLYING TIRE TO RIM

CHAPTER 13 § TESTING WIRE AND BEADS

EXAMINATION AND testing of wire and of the bead-grommet, before and after it is incorporated into the tire, is done for the purpose of maintaining quality, of determining whether a certain lot of wire meets specifications, and of predicting future behavior or finding causes of past failures.

Tensile-Elongation Test. This test measures the stress-strain characteristics of a sample of wire. It is run by stretching a 10-inch length of wire, clamped between the steel jaws of a testing machine, at a uniform rate until it breaks. A Scott testing machine is usually used for bead wire. One of its jaws is moved by a motor. The other is connected to a pointer, which indicates, on a dial, the pull in pounds. As the movable lower jaw travels downward, the elongation of the wire is recorded, as a curve, by a stylus moving against a paper-covered drum. The load or tension on the wire at any particular elongation is indicated by the dial.

The ultimate tensile strength is the load on the wire at the instant it breaks, as indicated by the weighing-mechanism pointer. The ultimate elongation is the total percentage of length increase at the moment of breaking and is recorded on the paper covering the drum. Tensile strength is calculated on the basis of the original area of the wire.

Olsen and Reihle Testing Machines. These tensile machines, which antedate the Scott, are used for determining the tensile characteristics of heavy wire and rods, materials beyond the capacity of the Scott machine. The weighing mechanism is a sliding-weight and beam combination. An Olsen machine, equipped with a bulldozer head, is shown on page 175.

Torsion Tests. Bead wire normally is not torsioned (twisted) in any manner in the manufacturing of the bead, in mounting or demounting the tire, or by forces affecting the bead while the tire is in service.

174

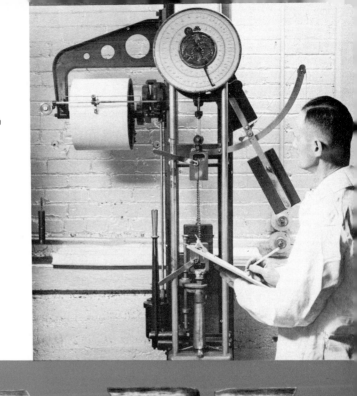

The extent to which a conventional torsion test relates to the service requirements of bead wire has been a controversial subject among engineers for some time. Early specifications included a torsion clause requiring that the wire withstand a specified number of turns per 100 diameters of length, or per some other arbitrarily specified length.

Bulldozer. In the tire-bead field, a bulldozer is a machine for expanding bead-grommets. The Olsen tensile machine has been modified for use in thus "bulldozing" bead-grommets in a tire, for the purpose of determining their strength. The bead to be tested is placed on the proper diameter of a sectional stepped chuck. This chuck resembles a flat-belt cone pulley that has been cut, like a pie, into eight equal pieces. An octagonal wedge moving downward at the chuck center causes the segments to move outward, thus expanding the bead-grommet. The pull or tensile stress applied to the hoop, or bead-grommet, is determined by the weighing mechanism of the Olsen machine. The elongation of the hoop circumference is indicated, in thousandths of an inch, by a counter, whose mechanism is linked to the screw operating the wedge.

Usually a test is run to the bursting point of the bead-grommet so that a stress-strain curve, up to the ultimate elongation and tensile strength, can be plotted. But before a set of values representing stress-strain characteristics of the wire bead-grommet can be obtained, enough force must be applied to compress the fabric and the rubber under it (around the inner circumference of the bead) until they become rigid. The tension applied to the bead as a whole is twice that at any one point on the bead circumference, since the bead is a ring.

The bulldozing action was applied to the Pratt bead-grommet and other cable-type reinforcements for the purpose of equalizing tension among the strands, removing kinks, making the ring truly round, and "setting" the cable so it became virtually as rigid as a rod.

Plating Tests. It is important to know the amount of copper or other metal on a given length of metal-coated wire. Thus a wire having a bronze-plate finish is checked to determine whether the plating is too light or heavier than need be. A quick method is to immerse a known length of wire in an electrolytic solution and deplate it. The hydrogen and oxygen gas liberated at the electrodes in the process are collected, and their volume measured. The deplating of bronze-plate wire finish requires only a fraction of a minute. The instant all copper has been removed from the steel is indicated by a sharp change in resistance between wire and solution, and the current is turned off to prevent the further formation of gas. The amount of copper removed is indicated by the amount of gas collected.

A more accurate but slower method consists of transferring the copper from a known length of wire to a platinum-mesh basket whose weight is known to close limits. The copper is stripped from the wire with acid and then plated on the platinum cathode basket from this solution. After the copper has been plated on the platinum, the basket is washed and dried, and then weighed. The increase in weight indicates the weight of copper on the wire, and from this the thickness of the plating can be calculated. The platinum basket is cleaned to remove the copper deposit and used again.

Tinning Test. A test, developed many years ago, for detecting pinholes and breaks in tinned iron or steel wire depends on color developed in a gelatin mass. A test solution is prepared by dissolving 25 grams of uncolored gelatin in 225 grams of water at 90°C. This is heated to boiling, and 0.2 gram of potassium ferricyanide [$K_3Fe(CN)_6$] added. The solution is cooled to 40°C. The wire to be tested is cleaned with a 5 per cent solution of sulfuric acid by immersion for 1 minute. It is dried, and its ends are dipped into molten paraffin to coat the exposed iron. Next, the wire is placed in the gelatin test solution. At the end of 15 minutes, a blue discoloration is visible on the wire wherever the iron was exposed by a pinhole or break in the tin coating. The gelatin solution is discarded after each test.

One manufacturer, who used the test for checking 0.054-inch double-tinned wire around 1930, had the following schedule for determining acceptability:

1. No discoloration visible: Good.
2. Few pinholes, widely distributed: Fair.
3. Scratches and pinholes, localized: Poor.
4. Considerable discoloration over practically entire wire surface: Very poor.

Tinning showing **condition** No. 1 or 2 was considered acceptable.

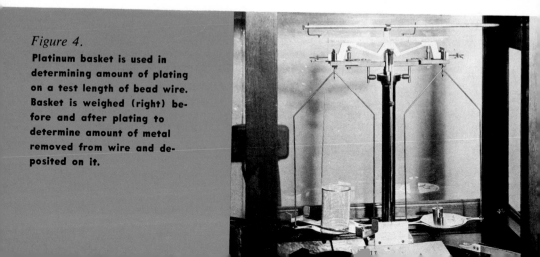

Figure 4.

Platinum basket is used in determining amount of plating on a test length of bead wire. Basket is weighed (right) before and after plating to determine amount of metal removed from wire and deposited on it.

Fluoroscope Test. One of the most helpful machines in determining causes of bead failure in a tire or conditions which ultimately might lead to failure, is an industrial X-ray unit. The tire is mounted on a stand that can be rotated to bring any part of the tire beads into the beam from an X-ray tube. The image is formed on a fluoroscope screen for visual studying. When a permanent record is to be obtained, a photographic film is inserted in place of the screen. This machine easily reveals such hidden flaws as kinked wire in a bead-grommet, separated wires at the lap, and oversized bead-grommets.

The "Bone" Test. The degree of "bone" in a piece of wire is a measure of its rigidity. At one time it was thought that by knowing the degree of bone in a wire its qualifications for making good tire beads could be determined. In later years this idea was supplanted by other physical tests that are more easily made and are far more conclusive. One of the first bone testers was made by bending a rectangular iron bar into a semicircle having a radius equivalent to the diameter of the wire test specimen multiplied by 100. At 8 inches from one end was mounted a scale having $\frac{1}{4}$-inch graduations. A means of clamping one end of the test wire to one end of the semicircle was provided. The test wire was a sample about 11 inches long taken from the lot of wire being checked. The wire was bent gradually through 180 degrees around the semicircular bar; then permitted to return gradually until it remained stationary. The reading on the scale at this point of operation indicated the amount of bend, or permanent set, the wire had taken. Today, there is a precision-built machine, as shown in Figure 7, weighted and calibrated to give reasonable accuracy and, therefore, reproducible results, available for testing wire stiffness. It has two scales, one used as a guide for varying the degree of bend, and one to give a reading of permanent set or recovery. A machine such as this is used primarily in testing wires where spring characteristics are desired.

Obviously, a wire having a high degree of bone, or rigidity, will, after being bent, return more nearly to its initial position than one that has less bone, or stiffness.

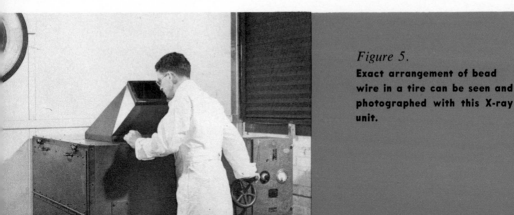

Figure 5.

Exact arrangement of bead wire in a tire can be seen and photographed with this X-ray unit.

Figure 6.

X-ray pictures of automobile tires showing (left) poor bead construction because wire ends were not properly anchored and (right) kinks in wire caused by careless handling during manufacture.

Other Testing Equipment. The Kenyon corrosion-fatigue testing method has been described in Chapter 11. Other tests used on bead wire include intermittent-corrosion studies, in which wire samples are alternately immersed in corroding agents and exposed to air. Microscopic and photomicrographic studies are used to check grain structure of steel, effects of stresses on crystalline structure, soundness of coatings, actions of corroding agents, and so on.

Road Tests. The final court for judging a tire bead is often located on the highway. By actually using the tire and therefore its beads, the effects of countless kinds and degrees of stresses, of corroding influences, and of other service conditions can be evaluated. Tire manufacturers maintain large fleets of test cars for determining the behavior of all parts of tires in production and those still in the development stage. Studies of casings whose beads have failed in normal service have revealed more than one valuable fact about bead behavior.

Excessive-sway Road Test. The bead of a tire must be sufficiently strong and properly engineered to enable it to outlast all other parts of the tire. Because of this, it is extremely difficult to organize a testing procedure that will cause the bead to fail before some other part of the tire separates or breaks down as a result of fatigue.

One test that has been employed successfully in deliberately causing beads to fail consists of running a single tire on dual-wheel equipment. The payload is jacked up or raised high above the axle so as to create excessive sway, and a test route that has many curves is specially selected.

179

A fairly high rate of speed must be maintained throughout the test. There is considerable danger that the swaying vehicle will get out of control and overturn if it happens to be coming into a curve at the moment of bead failure. To counteract this hazard, it is the practice to mount, on the dual-wheel rim adjacent to the tire being tested, another tire of the same rim diameter but smaller in section. The tread surface of this second tire normally does not come into contact with the road until such time as the test tire is deflated. Then the safety tire contacts the road, takes over the axle load, and permits the operator to bring the test truck to a stop with reasonable safety.

This safety arrangement, whereby a second tire stands by to take over the load the instant the test tire fails, is applied not only to bead testing but also to many other tests where complete tire failure may occur.

Hydraulic Tests. The ability of a tire's beads to withstand the tension produced by inflation pressure is judged by mounting the tire on a special rim and inflating it by hydraulic pressure instead of air. This pressure is greater than the normal operating pressure carried in the tire. An airplane tire, for example, may get a passing grade if its beads remain intact when the tire is hydraulically inflated to four times the operating pressure. That is, the beads have a safety factor of four. In comparison, a passenger-automobile tire bead can withstand, on the average, a hydraulic pressure of 250 pounds per square inch, indicating a safety factor of 10. Hydraulic

Figure 7.
Tinius Olsen stiffness tester.

pressure is used for testing instead of air primarily because, if a tire should burst, the resulting explosive action is less hazardous to surrounding equipment and personnel.

Rubber-to-Wire Adhesion Test. The adhesion between rubber and bead wire is tested by pulling samples of wire from blocks of rubber in which they have been cured. The test block measures ½ by 4 by 5 inches. Along one 5-inch edge of the mold are eight slots, cut down from the top. These slots accommodate hairpin-shaped anchor wires. Along the opposite 5-inch edge are four similar slots.

To prepare a test block, the mold is first half-filled with uncured rubber. Four hairpin-shaped anchor wires are placed in the eight slots along one edge, each bridging two slots and having its points inside the mold. Test wires are placed in the four opposite slots, their ends each lying between two anchor wires. A second layer of rubber is placed in the mold to fill it and cover the wires. The cover (male portion) of the mold is placed, and the assembly put into a vulcanizer. After being cured, the test block is permitted to cool from 4 to 8 hours before adhesion tests are run. Such tests can take place at any time up to 3 years or so after the rubber has been cured, for the adhesion does not change appreciably in that time in a specimen of rubber not in service.

To determine the degree of adhesion between the test wires and the rubber, the anchor wires are clamped in one jaw of a tensile-testing machine, and a test wire is grasped by the other jaw. One jaw is moved away from the other until the test wire separates from the rubber. Because the anchor wires are more numerous, test wires always separate first.

In such a test, two results are recorded: (1) The number of pounds pull required to separate the test wire from the rubber. (2) The degree of adhesion as judged by visual examination of the test wire after its removal. (See Judging Adhesion in Chapter 10.)

ENGINEERING SURVEY

Some years ago A. J. Pennington, of Cuyahoga Falls, Ohio, made a survey among prominent tire designers and engineers on the subject of beads. Answers to the questions that were put to these men reflected the problems and thoughts concerning various bead-making practices that were of importance at that time, and which generally are of no less concern today.

In composite form, answers to the question, "What constitutes a perfect bead-grommet?" looked somewhat like this:

The bead-grommet should be of adequate strength: with sufficient factor of safety to withstand all service conditions.

It should be anchored firmly in the tire and have a surface or construction to which rubber insulation or covering will adhere perfectly.

The bead-grommet should have a wire bundle properly proportioned and capable of retaining its shape throughout its positioning and during the curing of the tire.

It should be practically inextensible in order to hold the tire on the rim; yet at the same time it should be flexible enough to facilitate mounting.

Other questions brought out the fact that high-tensile steel wire is the best material yet found for making a bead-grommet that will still be intact when the tire is worn out.

One question sought to determine what form the wire should take in order to conform to the prerequisites of the perfect bead-grommet: it brought out the fact that flat-braided wire was the best bead-grommet material that had been developed. The reason for this was effectively summarized by one prominent engineer as follows:

Just "steel wire" is not enough. It should be a high-grade, high-tensile steel wire, braided flat to give all-direction flexibility—to avoid kinking of the individual wires not only during application of the bead-grommet to the tire but also while the tire is stored prior to curing and while it is in the process of being cured. The wires should be properly coated or plated to relieve the possibility of rust or corrosion between the supplier and the user; and, even more important, to insure a good bond between the wire and the rubber insulating stock. The insulating stock should be of such properties that it will extrude smoothly to give complete coverage without holes; and it must be sufficiently plastic to flow into the hundreds of interstices of the braided wire to produce a mechanical clinch or bond.

It was the unanimous feeling that without the proper application of textiles or the use of proper types of rubber compounds surrounding the bead-grommet a failure may result. Therefore, to ensure against tire failure in the bead region, a perfect bead-grommet must be used in proper surroundings.

Since the time these questions were proposed to the tire technicians, many changes have taken place. Rims have become wider, and smaller in diameter. Air pressures have been lowered. Automobile speeds have increased greatly. Still, the conditions reflected in the answers to Mr. Pennington's questions apply to the many bead requirements existing today, and many of the suggestions made in response to his inquiry have become standard practice.

CHAPTER 14 § OTHER USES FOR WIRE

WITH RUBBER

T IRE BEADS are but one example of how wire and rubber work together. The strength of wire reinforcement contributes to the performance abilities of such other products as high-pressure rubber hose, suction hose, tubing, airplane deicers, conveyor belts, V-belts, and electric cables. And wire is used in tires for purposes other than holding them on wheel rims.

Other Wire in a Tire. Fine wire strand to replace fabric cords in the carcasses of automobile tires—particularly those subjected to severe bruising forces, such as truck and bus casings—has been the subject of considerable research and development. This use of wire is not new and was tried 30 or so years ago. Of the innumerable constructions studied, the one found to be most promising on the basis of adhesion between wire and rubber and from the standpoint of long flex life was this: three fine wires twisted together to make a strand; seven of these strands combined to make a 7 by 3 rope—that is, six strands spiraled around a single center strand. A variation which proved satisfactory is a 6 by 3 rope consisting of six of the three-wire strands spiraled around a nonmetallic core. Rubber adhesion is achieved largely by brass-plating the wire. There is also some mechanical adhesion resulting from the porosity of the rope.

Various ways of employing wire in tire treads, in attempts to achieve better traction and stopping ability on ice and other slippery surfaces, have been devised. One method is to embed round helical coils of wire in the tread rubber so that one side of the helix is flush with the tread surface. As the wire wears, each turn becomes a C-shaped element, and its exposed ends are supposed to produce improved gripping action on slippery surfaces. Another system uses a device for placing short coils of wire in a tire tread so that one end of each coil is exposed to the road.

Wire has been similarly incorporated into the treads of airplane tires for the purpose of increasing traction to permit better braking action on ice and other slippery surfaces.

Wire in Hose and Tubing. Wire is used in rubber hose and tubing in a number of ways and for several purposes. Braided-wire covering incorporated in flexible hose and tubing adds to the bursting strength and may serve as a mechanical protection against abuse and wear. Sea-loading hose is heavily reinforced by spiral bands of flat wire on outer and inner surfaces and round wire between intermediate plies. Hydraulic-control and greasing hose have plies of fine steel wire, braided in a manner to produce maximum burst-resistance and placed between plies of rubber. Hose designed for various types of suction service are reinforced by spirals of stiff steel wire to prevent collapse. Wire also is used as a reinforcement in hose which might be run over by trucks or otherwise subjected to crushing action. One of the most complex types of hose is that used in rotary drilling of oil wells, etc. Several plies of metallic-mesh tape (or Pierce tape) enable the hose to withstand great internal pressure, and a wire spiral beneath the outer cover increases stiffness and strength.

Wire in Belting. Wire is used instead of fabric cords in flat rubber transmission and conveyor belting where high operating tensions must

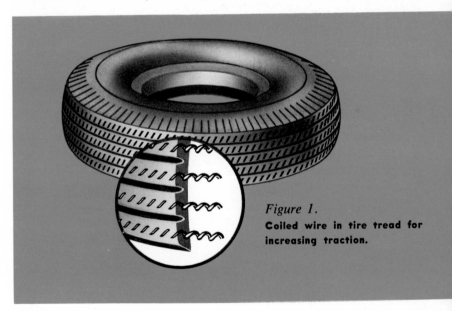

Figure 1.
Coiled wire in tire tread for increasing traction.

be maintained. Steel-cord conveyor belts, having strong, flexible steel cables running lengthwise, are used for hauling coal, ore, rock, and other heavy materials. Wire-reinforced V-belts are used where high strength and resistance to heat and stretching are required. The reinforcement is made of fine wire strands fabricated into endless cables or cords. Such V-belts replaced troublesome textile-reinforced belts on tanks operating during the North African campaign and in other phases of World War II.

Cable Covering. Wire is used for braided coverings on ignition and other types of electrical cables. Besides increasing strength and resistance to damage, the wire covering also may serve as an electrical shield, as in a microphone cable.

Drawn wire for these and other specialized purposes is manufactured in sizes ranging down to 0.002 inch in diameter, and in materials that included high- and low-carbon steel, stainless steel, aluminum, brass, copper, beryllium copper, monel metal, nickel silver, phosphor bronze, and numerous special-purpose alloys.

Some Uses for Braid. Other than as a reinforcement for tire beads, flat wire braid can be used as:

Reinforcement for high-pressure hose.
Reinforcement and nailing strip in rubber gaskets.

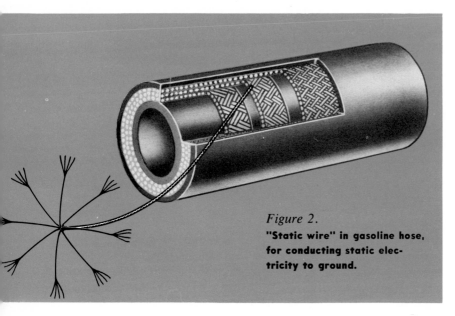

Figure 2.
"Static wire" in gasoline hose, for conducting static electricity to ground.

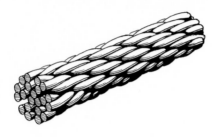

Figure 3.
Seven by three metallic strand, brass-plated (wire rope) of type used in tire carcass.

Figure 4.
Rubber hose showing braided-wire reinforcement.

Decorative inclusion and reinforcement in transparent plastic articles: the braid can be expanded to become open-mesh.

Baskets, lamps, jewelry, and other specialty items.

Decorative trim for furniture, etc.

Braid can be made of various metals to meet application requirements.

In tubular wire braid, the wires are braided together to form a cylinder or tube—as contrasted with flat wire braid, in which the wires form a ribbon or tape. Tubular wire braid is adaptable to many uses. These include (1) covering for flexible metal tubing, (2) reinforcement in rubber hose for high-pressure service, and (3) flexible storage-battery cable, a beamed-wire type of tubular braid being flattened to form a rectangular cross section.

A beamed-wire braid is one in which groups of several wires each are braided together. The conventional type is made by braiding individual wires.

Some Uses for Pierce Tape. In addition to its use as a reinforcement in tire beads, Pierce tape is employed as a reinforcement in rotary-drilling hose.

Straightness of Wire. Regardless of the form of application, all wire should be straight before it is processed into the final product. This is particularly true in the case of weftless tape used as bead reinforcement. Here the uncured-rubber insulating stock is the only medium holding the wires in place until they are incorporated into the tire and the rubber is cured.

Figure 5.
Conveyor belting using steel-cable reinforcement.

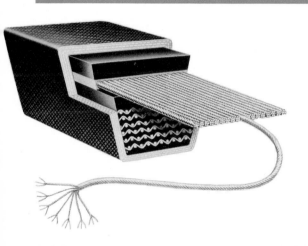

Figure 6.
One type of V-belt construction employing stranded steel wire which increases strength and reduces stretching.

Figure 7.
Flat wire braid can be expanded for various special applications.

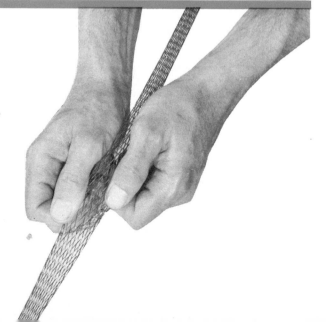

Figure 8.

**Installing inner-seal sponge
rubber weather stripping
having interwoven cord and
spring-wire tacking strip.
Bends are easily made at
corners without cutting
sponge-rubber bead. Wire
holds stripping in sealing position; yet permits some movement. (*Photo from Bridgeport
Fabrics, Inc.*)**

Figure 9.

**Wire-reinforced weather strip-
ping (Windlace) used around
automobile doors and for
other applications.**

Bicycle beads are an example of wire use where straightness is important. In such beads, as few as two strands of wire are plied up to form the bead-grommet, and extreme care must be taken to keep the wires straight. One crooked wire, which would represent 50 per cent of the wires involved, would distort the bead-grommet and greatly affect its roundness. This would result in building and curing difficulties.

Future Developments. Wire used in combination with rubber in tire beads and other constructions has, in the past, been the subject of extensive research. Such studies can be expected to continue, for although great progress has been made with respect to such things as the adhesion between wire and rubber, a state of perfection has not yet been reached. Future wire developments can be expected to take a number of directions. These will be aimed at such goals as the reduction or elimination of corrosion, improvement of adhesion with rubber and rubberlike materials, lowering of manufacturing costs, improved manufacturing techniques—aimed at such cost-lowering and at the production of better products in less time, and promotion of new ways of employing wire in combination with rubber and plastics.

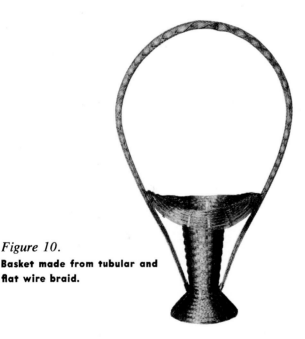

Figure 10.
Basket made from tubular and flat wire braid.

AMONG THE BOOKS which have mentioned tire types, beads, and rims are the following:

"Rubber Tires," by Henry C. Pearson, India Rubber Publishing Company (1906); "Pneumatic Tires," by same author (1922).

"The History of the Pneumatic Tyre," by J. B. Dunlop, Alex. Thom and Co., Ltd., Dublin.

"Diamond Tires" and "Best in the Long Run," published by The B. F. Goodrich Company (1918).

"The Reign of Rubber," by William C. Geer, The Century Company, New York.

"The Story of Rubber," by Dr. R. J. Tudor, The Burke Publishing Company, Ltd., London.

"The Romance and Drama of the Rubber Industry," by Harvey S. Firestone, Jr. (radio talks).

"L'Industrie du caoutchouc," by Fernard Jacobs (1923).

"Wheels of Fortune," by Sir Arthur du Cros, Bt., Chapman and Hall, Ltd., London (1938).

"The Firestone Story," by Alfred Lief, Whittlesey House, McGraw-Hill Book Company, Inc., New York (1951).

"The House of Goodyear," by Hugh Allen, Corday and Gross Company, Cleveland, Ohio (1949) (Also earlier editions).

Patent abridgments and other patent literature of Great Britain, France, Germany, and the United States.

"The Encyclopaedia Britannica."

Back numbers of such magazines as *The Autocar* and *India Rubber World*.

INDEX

xz